RESPONSIBLY DRIVEN
AN IMPAIRED DRIVING PREVENTION CURRICULUM

Copyright © 2021 Jonathan P. M. Barber and Eric K. Dungan

All rights reserved. No part of this book may be reproduced in any written, electronic, recording, or photocopying form without written permission from the publisher. Please do not participate in or encourage piracy of copyrighted materials in violation of the author's rights. Purchase only authorized editions.

ISBN: 978-0-99977662-2-4

10 9 8 7 6 5 4 3 2 1

Printed in the United States of America
Library of Congress Control Number: 2020922449
Author: Jonathan P. M. Barber and Eric K. Dungan
Edited by Fiesta Publishing
Cover Design and Interior Layout: Alli Masi

Fiesta Publishing
www.fiestapublishing.com

DEDICATION

In memory of those individuals tragically killed and/or injured by an impaired driver.

TABLE OF CONTENTS

Foreword 1

Lessons

    Introduction: "How Did I Get Here?" 3

    Lesson 1: Honesty 6

    Lesson 2: Denial 11

    Lesson 3: Relationship with Alcohol, Drugs, and Impaired Driving 17

    Lesson 4: Responsibility and Underlying Issues 21

    Lesson 5: "Is it Safe for Me to Drink Again?" 27

    Lesson 6: Personal Sobriety 31

    Lesson 7: Developing Empathy 35

    Lesson 8: The Consequences of Impaired Driving 41

    Lesson 9: *CS3 Sobriety Plan* Preparation 45

    Lesson 10: *CS3 Sobriety Plan* Presentations 47

Acknowledgments 49

Bibliography 51

Appendices

    Appendix A: *CS3 Sobriety Plan* Template 57

    Appendix B: Facilitator Guide 61

    Appendix C: Personal Testimonials

        Personal Testimonial 1: Eric D. 91

        Personal Testimonial 2: Jonathan B. 93

    Appendix D: Tables

        Table 1: Blood Alcohol Concentration (BAC) Levels 97

        Table 2: The Progressive Effects of Alcohol 99

FOREWORD

Responsibly Driven (RD) was created by impaired driving offenders for the purpose of affecting long-term change in other offenders who have been arrested and those who are at risk of driving impaired[1]. Our firsthand knowledge and experience have allowed for the development and delivery of a curriculum that meets other offenders at their level of responsibility while challenging their destructive beliefs and behaviors. The program's uniqueness is our approach to impaired driving prevention. Our program helps participants identify and address their underlying issues with impaired driving through our *Clean, Sober, Safe, and Sustainable (CS3) Sobriety Plan*. **Responsibly Driven** participants who complete the program leave with a clean, sober, safe, and sustainable approach to sobriety and impaired driving.

"It will never happen to me" is a common thought amongst impaired drivers. Throughout our years of driving intoxicated, the founding members of **Responsibly Driven** entertained this distorted belief. It gave us permission to abuse alcohol/drugs and then to drive in a car. We were unwilling to examine our selfish decisions, because we refused to acknowledge the reality that impaired driving is inherently deadly. We believed that we were "special" and immune from such travesties. But everything changed in 2014 with the formation of **Responsibly Driven.**

The creation of **Responsibly Driven** and its curriculum filled a void for us that was missing from our past attempts at change. Despite multiple encounters with law enforcement agents, DUI courts, and impaired driving schools, our denial proved impenetrable in the midst of the self-induced chaos, admonitions, and the implementation of punishments. Yet, we could no longer hide behind our delusions when confronted by fellow DUI offenders who found a way to be accountable for their past and present actions. These conversations created a situational context conducive for honest introspection. We found that this approach fueled everyone's desire for accountability, authenticity, and contrition.[2]

For those facilitators who have no prior history of impaired driving, we strongly encourage a review of one's life. At some point in our lives, we all have entertained some distorted thought patterns and/or behaved in counterproductive ways. Use those experiences as a resource in your group discussions. Be willing to share your failures and vulnerabilities. Your courageous

---

[1] **Responsible Driven** has chosen to use the term *impaired driving* to highlight all dangerous forms of driving. Impaired driving is commonly known as driving under the influence (DUI), driving while intoxicated/impaired (DWI), or operating a motor vehicle while intoxicated or under the influence (OWI), but it is also important to recognize a DUI driver shares many of the distorted thinking patterns with other dangerous drivers (i.e., distracted driving). This curriculum addresses the core destructive issues all said drivers possess.

introspection and revelation demonstrates relatability and humility. It shows a genuineness of a person who cares, not a person who is trying to "fix" someone. When we effectively facilitate in this manner, participants will view us as someone walking beside them in their quest for self-discovery.

Many of us who were founding members of **Responsibly Driven** and serving indeterminate sentences have been paroled from California's correctional system since 2014. We are now law-abiding citizens who actively engage in our communities and seek ways to sow value in all of our relationships. We have adopted responsible life perspectives that provide us opportunities we once took for granted. Furthermore, we seek to enhance the lives of others and to honor those tragically killed by the reckless and selfish decision to drive impaired. By passing on the knowledge and tools that supported our transformations, we look to support positive change in the lives of those individuals struggling with similar issues. By convincing one person not to drive impaired, we save one life thereby preserving one family.

- Jonathan P.M. Barber
CADC II, SUDCC III

---

[2] For those reasons, we have elected to use a first-person writing style. A second- or third-person writing style often presents a disconnected point of view as it presents an outsider's perspective. When being spoken to as "you" a reader's defensive mechanism of denial quickly activates. It creates resistance, hence a refusal to consider feedback and new perspectives is produced. In extreme cases, the reader may feel that he/she is being judged or is the focus of condescendence. Such a situational context is not advantageous for a transformative conversation.

The first-person point of view writing style is a valuable tool. With this style, we communicate to our participants that they are not alone nor that their experience is unique. It conveys that we understand their plight, because we have "been there, done that". Through establishing this vital connection **Responsibly Driven** offers participants hope for their redemptive transformations.

INTRODUCTION: "HOW DID I GET HERE?"

*In 2016, more than one million drivers were arrested
for driving under the influence of alcohol or narcotics.*
(United States Department of Justice, *Crime in the United States 2016: Uniform Crime Reports*)

If you want something you've never had, then you've got to do something you've never done.
Thomas Jefferson

• • •

Welcome to **Responsibly Driven (RD)**. **RD** is a comprehensive rehabilitative program that seeks to prevent impaired driving by empowering individuals to uncover and treat the underlying issues and their destructive behavior of impaired driving and substance abuse. **RD** views impaired driving as a series of bad choices. We make a choice to become intoxicated, then an additional choice to drive while intoxicated. The purpose of **RD** is to help individuals understand both of these choices and, with this understanding, create a plan that ensures they never drive impaired again.

In 2018, 10,511 people died in alcohol-impaired auto collisions (US Depart. of Transportation, *Traffic Safety Facts 2018, 1*), and more than one million drivers were arrested for driving under the influence of alcohol or narcotics (US Depart. of Justice, *Crime in the United States 2016: Uniform Crime Reports* n. pag.). We believe these numbers can and should be zero. As members of **RD**, we seek to raise awareness of the destructive force this preventable tragedy afflicts upon victims and survivors, families, and our communities. Over the next ten sessions, our goal is to create an environment that promotes positive change towards these goals through education and small group sessions.

Small Group Guidelines

1. Confidentially must be strictly observed by all members. What is said in the group stays in the group.
2. Be respectful of one another.
3. Keep your sharing focused on yourself.
4. No side-talk. Side-talk is when two or more individuals engage in conversation with themselves separate from the group.
5. Be willing to consider new perspectives and tools.
6. Be open to feedback.

Character of Small Group

Our small group discussions will be conducted in an atmosphere of trust, confidentiality, and shared commitment. Over the next ten sessions, we will be working towards the individual goal of a *clean, sober, safe,* and *sustainable* sobriety. For this goal to be achieved, each participant must come prepared. Self-effort is the only means of producing a lasting sobriety. This process begins with each participant coming to the group prepared to do the necessary work to effect positive change in his/her life. Group participants should review each upcoming lesson as well as completing the previous lesson's assignment. We encourage participants to ask questions as we navigate through these concepts and perspectives.

Getting Started: Your Personal Story

Through our program's step-by-step process, we will identify our underlying issues and create a solid, durable sobriety plan. Today, we will take the first step towards sobriety by getting to know each other, beginning with simple question: "How Did I Get Here?"

Questions:

1. Why are you in **Responsibly Driven?**

_____
_____
_____
_____
_____
_____
_____

2. What do you hope to gain from the class?

_____
_____
_____
_____
_____
_____
_____

3. What are you willing to change to achieve that goal?

_____
_____
_____
_____
_____
_____
_____

LESSON 1: HONESTY

More than twenty-nine million people in the United States admitted to driving impaired in the past year. (Lomurro)

Honesty is an active verb, not a passive noun. Go out of your way to be truthful, beginning with the things that you say to yourself.
Joe Tye

• • •

One day Fredrick the Great, King of Prussia, visited a prison and talked with each of the inmates. There were endless tales of innocence, misunderstood motives, and exploitations. Finally the king stopped at the cell of a convict who remained silent.

"Well," remarked Frederick, "I suppose you are an innocent victim too?"
"No, sir, I'm not," replied the man. "I'm guilty and deserve my punishment."

Turning to the warden, the king said, "Here, release this rascal before he corrupts all these fine innocent people in here!" (Golson Jr. 216).

The story of the king and a prisoner brings to life the essential principle for change: honesty. Honesty is the foundation of positive change. It uncovers our deceptions, enables and supports our self-development, and points us toward higher levels of thought and decision making. For us to change, we must choose to embrace honesty. Honesty must become a part of our character in a way that is understood, seen, and felt. Because what is true is true in spite of our deceptions, the benefits of acknowledging truth can only be positive while our efforts to ignore it will continue to be negative. Said differently, just because you believe driving impaired is "no big deal" does not make it true.

When we commit ourselves to living honestly, we are agreeing to see ourselves and the world as they truly are, not as we would have them. When we see and accept things as they are, we encourage right action and a greater connection with ourselves and the world around us. When we lie, however, we cut ourselves off from this bigger picture. We become isolated, defensively pushing away anything that could expose us to the truth and surrounding ourselves with things that support our lies.

Creating a mindset that supports honesty will help us break from our constant need to be right. This process starts with us evaluating our actions, thoughts, and beliefs, and then asking if these things are really true. "Is it okay for me to drive impaired?" "Do I have a problem with alcohol/drugs?" "How did I get here?" These are questions we must have the courage to not only ask ourselves, but also to answer – honestly.

There is no quick fix to becoming more honest. We develop the habit of being honest by practicing honesty. Thankfully, honesty is empowering and contagious. One honest moment creates space for more honesty. The more we practice honesty, the more we will find others around us becoming more truthful. Try it for yourself. Give an honest statement to someone you encounter today and see what happens. Often, you will find that your honest statement is immediately followed by another honest statement from your counterpart. Honesty begets more honesty.

For all its gifts, honesty can be challenging to channel in the moment. We lie for a reason. In the moment, a lie can feel like the perfect way to impress someone, to get what we want, and to avoid uncomfortable moments and/or negative consequences. Yet, every lie has a price.

Lies damage us. The act of keeping a lie alive means that we must live in constant conflict with reality. A lie can only be kept alive by another lie. As we continue down this path of deception, the burden grows heavier and its consequences worsen. When we hear a person say, "I can drive drunk because I'm a good drunk driver," we know such a statement cannot exist on its own. It lives within a vast web of dishonesty. Thankfully, one honest moment can give us the clarity that we need to identify the falsity of our thoughts.

An essential tool in gaining this clarity is the ability to see our actions through the eyes of others. This technique allows us to separate from the emotions and thoughts we use to justify our actions, thereby giving us the necessary space to view our actions in a more objective (honest) light. Victor Frankl spoke of such a technique when making choices:

> *So live as if you were living already for the second time and as if you had acted the first time as wrongly as you are about to act now!*

In this example, Frankl encourages us to look at our actions as an older, wiser version of ourselves. By doing so, we separate from the person we are now in order for us to see ourselves from a different perspective. Notably, when we say *see* ourselves, we are seeing what is happening on the inside and the outside: both the act itself, in addition to the mindset (thoughts/beliefs) that enabled it. This technique could also work by choosing to see our actions through the eyes of a loving parent, a supportive friend, or a fictional person.

This practice gives us an opportunity to reflect upon our actions apart from our personal biases and sentiments. Free from these prejudices, we can ask ourselves the critical questions: "Do my actions reflect who I want to be?" and "Are my thoughts based on what is true?"

We will begin by viewing our decision to drive impaired. Throughout this exercise, we will pay attention not only to the action but also our rationalization of why it is okay for us to make these choices. We will have the opportunity to see our thoughts and actions from a different perspective. Afterward, we will discuss our experience with this activity and our thoughts on the lesson.

Honesty Exercise

Instructions: (Materials are listed in Appendix B: Facilitators Guide.)

Start by thinking back to a time when you made a choice to drive intoxicated. Remember the time and place, the people you were with, and what you were doing. With these thoughts in mind, grab the first sheet of paper and at the top write the phrase: "I can drive under the influence because..." (Pause) *With this stream of thought, continue writing for the next five minutes. Do not judge or critique your grammar. Do not worry about writing complete sentences. Simply jot down your thoughts about a time when you justified driving under the influence of alcohol/drugs. What were the thoughts, beliefs, and excuses you used to defend your actions?* (Pause for 5 Minutes)

After five minutes have elapsed, put that paper to the side and grab another sheet of paper. This time imagine you are someone else. This person can be someone you know or someone you never met. It could even be a future, wiser version of you. What is important is that this person be someone you respect and view as an honest judge of actions and character. With this person in mind, evaluate your choice to drive impaired. Begin by writing the phrase: "I see an intoxicated person walking to his/her car...". Write down the thoughts you believe this person would have. Describe what this person sees and what emotions they feel. (Pause) *Continue writing from this person's point of view for the next ten minutes. Write as you did before without a care for grammar or spelling.* (Pause for 10 Minutes)

Now, put both pages, one from each perspective, next to each other and review what you wrote. How do these two viewpoints differ? Which perspective is more accurate? How has the experience of seeing your actions from another person's perspective changed your thoughts about driving under the influence? (Long Pause)

Exercise Process

For the next fifteen minutes, we will discuss answers you came up with during the exercise among the group. Moreover, consider and share how you will apply your newly discovered insights to your daily life.

Questions:

1. What is honesty to you?

_____
_____
_____
_____
_____

2. Why should you practice honesty in your life?

___

3. Describe what you saw during your fifteen-minute visualization exercise.

___

4. Describe what you heard the visualization exercise. (What kind of reasons did you use to justify your actions?)

___

5. How has your opinion of these things changed when you saw them from another person's perspective?

___

6. Whose viewpoint is more accurate, the others person's perspective or yours? Why?

7. How would this experience look if you were practicing honesty?

8. How can you begin to practice honesty in your daily life?

LESSON 2: DENIAL

On average, a convicted drunk driver has driven drunk eighty times before his or her first arrest. (MADD)

Before you can lie to another, you must first lie to yourself.
Naval Ravikant

• • •

Now that we have talked about honesty, it is time to talk about its counterpart, denial. As we stated earlier the only way to keep a lie alive is with another lie. When we continue to live within these lies, we will find ourselves further and further separated from reality. In fact, we could say that we live in opposition with reality, or better said in denial of it.

Impaired driving is a choice we have all made. Before making this choice, we heard the warnings and knew the inherent dangers of driving while impaired, yet we persisted. Why? How is it that thousands of people every day make a choice to put themselves and those within their community at risk of injury and even death? Today, we will discuss the mechanism that facilitates these destructive choices – denial.

Definition of Denial

Denial is a system of false beliefs that are not based on reality. It is the "Big Lie" we tell ourselves to avoid uncomfortable feelings and to protect ourselves from the truth (Kipper 70).[3]

Do you hear yourself in any of these statements?

"I'm a good drunk driver."

"Somebody has to drive, and I'm the most sober."

"I don't have a problem. The doctor prescribed me these pills."

"I'm only going down the street."

"I only drank a few beers. It is not a big deal."

It is a big deal. Again and again, we witness the devastating consequences of impaired driving. Nevertheless, we fall back into our distorted thinking, "I only had a few drinks," or "I am just buzzed," instead of recognizing the simple truth – there is never an excuse to drive under the influence of alcohol or drugs.

---

[3]Terrance Gorski offers an extended definition of *denial* as, "a set of automatic [spontaneous] and unconscious [without thinking] thoughts, feelings, and actions that protects us from the pain of thinking about and talking about our problems" (Gorski n.pag.).

Why is It so Hard for Us to Admit We are Wrong?

Despite our best efforts, we will be wrong at times. It is going to happen. We are human; hence we make mistakes and bad decisions. Being wrong can be difficult to admit. This reality occurs often because being wrong conflicts with ideas we have about ourselves; ideas like "I am a caring person," or "I am intelligent". We experience stress when we make choices that conflict with such ideas. Psychologists coined the term *cognitive dissonance* to describe this experience of increased stress.

> "*Cognitive dissonance* is what we feel when the self-concept – I'm smart, I'm kind, I'm convinced this belief is true - is threatened by evidence that we did something that wasn't smart, that we did something that hurt another person, that the belief isn't true." (Aaronson n. pag.)

When we experience *cognitive dissonance* we can either choose to accept the evidence and admit we are wrong or deny fault and refuse ownership of our mistake. Unfortunately, many of us choose to stay entrenched in our beliefs and create elaborate justifications for our actions. We would describe a person behaving in this fashion as "being in denial." Yet, the person themselves may feel confident by stubbornly "sticking to their guns" and relieved by avoiding the uncomfortableness of admitting their wrongdoing. Despite the payoffs of our deception, reality has not changed nor do they make our actions less dangerous. It takes a person with a well-developed sense of self-esteem to admit they are mistaken. Together we will work to build confidence within ourselves to admit when we are wrong.

Do I Have a Problem?

It is difficult to admit we have a problem. Conventional thinking tells us that only alcoholics and addicts have problems with substance use; unfortunately, this reasoning could not be further from the truth. Even occasional recreational substance use, like drinking alcohol with a friend, can turn deadly if the participants are unaware of or disregard the dangers of driving under the influence of mind-altering substances. The answer to the question, "Do I have a problem?" requires honest introspection. We can begin this exploration by reviewing the results we receive in our lives. One result to consider is our current participation in this program. The fact that we are in an impaired driving program indicates that we need to make changes in our lives.

Understanding Addiction

Many of us have issues with the labels: "alcoholic" or "addict." Confronted with the stereotypic and stigmatized images of an alcoholic shaking as he battles to open another bottle of cheap booze or an addict slapping his veins about to insert a needle into his arm, we promptly declare, "That's not me!" Although these images may not reflect your actions or lifestyles that does not mean you are not suffering from addictions.

Substance dependency comes in varying degrees and stages. Some alcoholics/addicts may exhibit a psychological dependency. A psychological dependent may "exhibit uncontrollable emotional cravings for particular substance or activity. When deprived of it, [he/she] experiences feelings of loss and borderline unbearable uneasiness" (Mendelson 22-23).

A physical dependency occurs when a person is deprived of a particular substance and develops withdrawal symptoms. These physical symptoms may include nausea, vomiting, excessive perspiration, heart palpitations, irregular blood pressure, and bodily tremors (24). If you develop any of these symptoms after long periods of drinking alcohol or using drugs, you should immediately contact the proper medical authorities to help you safely detox.

Some alcoholics and addicts have physical withdrawals while others have psychological withdrawals. Some people experience both types of withdrawls. Having an absence in one area does not disqualify you from being an addict or alcoholic. "The chief expression of any addict is when the substance becomes the center point of your existence, overshadowing all other aspects of your life. If this is true, then for all intents and purposes you are an addict" (19). Substance dependency and abuse are inherent issues of alcohol and drug use. We should not allow the stigmas surrounding dependency prevent us from getting help. Make no mistake: addiction is a clearly defined health problem that must be treated to ensure long-term success (Kipper 1). Identifying and admitting our problem(s) is the first step towards fixing them.

Addiction is NOT a Necessary Component of Impaired Driving

It is important to recognize that alcoholism or drug addiction are not needed to become an impaired driver. Ask yourself these questions:

"Have I ever ignored the effects that alcohol and drugs had on my ability to drive?"
"Have I ever blacked out while drinking alcohol or using drugs?"
"Have I ever made dangerous choices while drinking alcohol or using drugs?"

Alcoholics and addicts are not the only people who make bad choices while intoxicated. Individually, we must all make an honest assessment of our relationship with alcohol/drugs and the actions we take while under the influence.

Reality Check

Simply put: <u>If you, no matter how rare, become intoxicated and then make the choice to put your life and the lives of others at risk by driving impaired, you have a problem.</u> Every year irresponsible choices involving intoxication and driving claim the lives of thousands of people in cities across the country. Now is the time to be accountable for your denial, your alcohol/drug usage, and the choices you make while impaired.

Questions

1. What areas in your life do you believe denial is most active?

_____
_____
_____
_____
_____
_____
_____

2. How has denial impacted your decision making?

_____
_____
_____
_____
_____
_____
_____

3. How does denial impact your relationships?

_____
_____
_____
_____
_____
_____
_____

4. In what ways have you used denial to continue destructive behaviors?

_____
_____
_____
_____
_____
_____
_____

5. Do you believe confronting denial is important? Explain.

_____
_____
_____
_____
_____
_____

6. How can you confront your denial?

_____
_____
_____
_____
_____
_____
_____

LESSON 3: RELATIONSHIP WITH ALCOHOL, DRUGS, AND IMPAIRED DRIVING

According to the 2019 National Survey on Drug Use and Health (NSDUH), 54.9 percent reported that they drank alcohol in the past month. 25.8 percent of people ages 18 or older reported that they engaged in binge drinking in the past month; 6.3 percent reported that they engaged in heavy alcohol use in the past month.[4] (US Department of Health and Human Services 1).

***A belief is not merely an idea the mind possesses, it is an idea that possesses the mind.*
Robert Oxten Bolt**

• • •

In this lesson, we will be discussing our relationship with alcohol/drugs and impaired driving. On the surface, this may seem like a strange topic. You may think, "I don't have a relationship with alcohol or drugs"; but is not a relationship just a series of interactions a person has with another person or thing, which over time fosters a connection between the two? Relationships have histories, feelings, and motives. They have rewards (the things we get out of the relationship) and consequences (the things we lose for maintaining the relationship). We drank alcohol/used drugs and drove because we get something out of it. . .What is it? Some different factors to consider while exploring these relationships are family, friends, entitlements and justifications, and self-identity.

Family

Families have a huge influence over our lives. From an early age, we establish behaviors by observing and imitating those individuals closest to us (Kipper 13). As we grow, we adopt our family's beliefs, values, and traditions, hence we inherit our family's unhealthy relationship with alcohol and drugs. Studies have shown that "children of alcoholics are seven times more likely to develop alcoholism than children of non-alcoholics" (Pollock, Schneider, Gabrielli, & Goodwin, 1987; Merkikangas, 1990). Studies have also shown a similar pattern for children of drug addicts (Mooney 470). For those of us struggling with addiction and the self-destructive actions we take while intoxicated, understanding our family's attitude towards alcohol/drugs and impaired driving is often the first step in understanding our own attitude.

---

[4] *Binge drinking* is defined as drinking four to five alcoholic beverages once in a thirty-30-day period whereas *heavy drink* is defined as five or more days of binge drinking in a thirty-day period (SAMSHA 1).

Friends

There are social aspects to substance use and impaired driving. Our friendships influence our patterns of drinking alcohol/using drugs and the actions we take while intoxicated. For those of us who drive impaired, our choice to be "social" often puts us in dangerous situations. We go out with friends – drink alcohol/use drugs – then decide to drive home.

For many, the most difficult part of changing our attitude towards alcohol and drugs will be dealing with those friends who once supported our substance use. We see these people as our friends, not a part of our problem. Unfortunately, it will be necessary to set up healthy boundaries and perhaps even separate from certain individuals whose behaviors negatively affect our choices.

Entitlements/Justifications

There are times we believe we have earned the right to do something: "I worked all week. I deserve a few drinks." or "It's my car, so I can drive it if I want." We may think that we are "better" or "unique," therefore entitled to special consideration: "I'm not like the rest of these drunks." These thoughts are entitlements. Other times we may believe there are certain things we must do: "It's Saint Patrick's Day. I have to get drunk today." or "I have to drive because no one else can." These types of thoughts are called justifications. Justifications often come in the form of circumstances or situations we use to excuse our actions. Many times, we use entitlements and justifications as excuses. They are the stories we tell ourselves to rationalize our decisions to drink alcohol/use drugs and drive impaired. No matter the accomplishment or special day, there is never a reason to drink alcohol/use drugs irresponsibly. Have you ever used occasions like holidays, birthdays, or work as an excuse to drink alcohol/use drugs or to drive impaired?

Self-Identity

How do You View Alcohol/Drugs and Impaired Driving?

Sometimes we imagine alcohol/drugs as social lubricants that help us celebrate weddings, reunions, and other special occasions. We may have fond memories of a drink we shared with a loved one or a night out at a bar with friends. On the other hand, alcohol and drugs contribute to thousands of deaths every year. There seems to be a disconnection between our personal beliefs about alcohol/drugs and its well-recognized potential for destroying lives. As a result, we may choose to overlook alcohol and drugs' negative effects and instead focus on their imagined benefits. Have you ever chosen to acknowledge only the positive aspects of drinking alcohol/using drugs or impaired driving while ignoring its negative consequences?

How do You Feel about Yourself when You Drink Alcohol/Use Drugs?

Many of us create parts of our identities through substance use. Men are often encouraged to drink, even to excess, as a sign of manliness. Most drinkers, regardless of gender, believe it is important to be able to "hold their liquor." Often, we use such beliefs to create the illusion of control despite actions to the contrary (i.e., driving impaired). This distorted thought only isolates us from the truth of our behavior. Alcohol works cumulatively. The more you drink alcohol the more intoxicated you become. Eventually, you hit a tipping point at which your "high" turns into sluggishness, fatigue, disorientation, or worse (Kipper 200).[5] Yet, we ironically see ourselves as getting stronger, funnier, and better looking the more intoxicated we become.

Alcohol and drugs do not make us better. They are chemicals that temporarily and artificially change the way we feel. There was never such a thing as a good drunk or user. Yet, we seem oblivious to the natural consequences of drinking alcohol and using drugs. Instead we are motivated by emotions and thoughts that we barely understand. Responsibility begins when we take ownership of our thoughts and beliefs. It is time to confront the falsehoods, influences, and motivations surrounding our drinking alcohol/using drugs and impaired driving.

Questions

1. How has your family influenced your attitude towards drinking alcohol/using drugs and impaired driving?

_____
_____
_____
_____
_____
_____
_____

2. How have your friends influenced your attitude towards drinking alcohol/using drugs and driving impaired?

_____
_____
_____
_____
_____

---

[5] For more information about the effects of alcohol refer to the tables in Appendix D.

3. What reasons do you use to justify your decisions to drink alcohol/use drug and then drive impaired?

_____
_____
_____
_____
_____
_____
_____

4. What do alcohol/drugs "fix"? What is wrong with the way you feel prior to using drinking alcohol/using drugs?

_____
_____
_____
_____
_____
_____
_____

5. How is drinking alcohol/using drugs and driving impaired attached to your self-identity?

_____
_____
_____
_____
_____
_____

LESSON 4: RESPONSIBILITY AND UNDERLYING ISSUES

Researchers found that the more strongly people believed that they could change, the more likely they were to take responsibility for their actions (Schumann n. pag.)

"If we change within, our outer life will change also."
Jean Shinoda Bolen

• • •

Responsibility

We all have a basic understanding of responsibility and how a responsible person should act. A responsible person makes informed, prosocial choices based upon a rational understanding of the world. A responsible person takes ownership of the choices he/she makes and the outcomes of his/her choices. A responsible person does not put others or him/herself in dangerous situations by driving under the influence of mind-altering substances.

For most of us, our problem is not understanding the concept of responsibility, but instead we struggle with living responsibly. We struggle because we have not gotten to the root of our problems: the underlying issues that reveal themselves outwardly through our destructive behavior. If we better understood why we make certain choices, we could prevent destructive decision-making and better support positive choices.

Impaired Driving is a Series of Choices

1. We make the choice to become intoxicated.
2. We make the choice to drive impaired.

We draw valuable insight by separating the choice we make to become intoxicated and the choice we make to drive impaired. The first choice involves our relationship with alcohol/drugs-"Am I a binge drinker?" "Do I have dependency issues?"- while the second choice aides us in understanding our mindset relative to our dangerous behavior. When you went out with friends to drink alcohol/use drugs, why did you not have a plan to get home safe? How did you rationalize driving impaired?

Understanding Your "Why"

As we search for our underlying issues, be mindful of the differences between "how," "what," and "why."

For example:

"I drink and drive because at the end of the night I am usually the most sober person."

This is not "why" you drink alcohol and drive impaired; this is your perception of what happens when you drink.

"I use because I like the feeling of being high."

That is not "why" you use drugs; this is how you feel when you use.

Think of it this way: if you are holding an apple in your hand and suddenly let it go, it will fall to the ground. "What" happened was that the apple hit ground. "How" it happened was your hand released it. However, "why" it happened is because of the law of gravity.

Similarly, our choices are influenced by our beliefs, coping mechanisms, and personal philosophies. These mechanisms are also invisible and have just as much control over our choices as gravity does a falling object. When we are talking about our "Why's", we are talking about how we use these mechanisms to relate and react to situations. Being able to talk about our "Why's" is essential to identifying our underlying issues.

What Are My Underlying Issues?

In order to help us uncover our underlying issues with impaired driving, we ask that you answer the following questions:

<u>What do I Believe?</u>

In the "Relationship with Alcohol, Drugs, and Impaired Driving" lesson, we investigated the thoughts that fueled our substance abuse. It is time now for us to connect those thoughts back to our beliefs.

What do I believe? Beliefs can be gained through learning and self-reflection, or they can be acquired passively. Beliefs that are gained passively are often referred to as unconscious beliefs. We acquire them by what we adopt from the world around us; however, these beliefs are outside of our awareness, therefore referred to as unconscious beliefs. It is this lack of awareness that we must now address.

It is not what happens to us that creates our thoughts, but a combination of what is happening and how we relate to these events via our beliefs. Events are filtered through our belief system, which in turn produces our thoughts and feelings. Beliefs therefore shape how we interact with ourselves and the outside world. This reality underscores the importance of our belief system. We are all at the mercy of our beliefs. It is not what happens to us, but our beliefs about these things and ourselves that determines how we think and feel.

If we are making the choice to drive impaired, then we must conclude that some of our beliefs are untrue and/or no longer serve us. Ideas that someone can be a "good drunk driver" or that "everybody does it" are beliefs based NOT on what is true. When we recognize that our distorted thoughts are rooted in beliefs that are not true, we can begin replacing them with what is true. What are the central underlying beliefs that facilitated your choice to drive under the influence?

What do I Feel?

Upon honest reflection, the question, "What do I feel?" reveals a lot about responsibility. It is well known that our beliefs are triggers for what we feel. Although we may have had negative experiences that led us to believe in things that were untrue, it is also important to recognize that we all had other experiences and information that told us that what we were doing was wrong. Yet, we choose to ignore it and instead created a belief system (both consciously and unconsciously) that supported our destructive choices.

"Why did I drive impaired?" In short, we did it because it felt "good". It may have felt "good" to go along with the crowd. It may have felt "good" to do what we wanted to do. It felt "good" to simply jump into the car and drive away, because we did not want to be inconvenienced. We should all reflect on that last sentence. We were willing to put other people's lives at risk because it was too inconvenient for us to find a safe way home. Whatever your reason, it is grounded in the fact that you got *something* out of driving impaired or you would have not put yourself at such a risk. So, what was the payoff? What felt "good" about driving impaired? What does impaired driving "fix"? This inquiry comes with a disclaimer: We identify these feelings not so that we can control how we feel. The purpose for identifying these feelings is for us to learn better ways to control ourselves the next time these feelings arise.

It is okay to not feel okay. We cannot always do what we want based upon how we feel. Being willing to deal with uncomfortable feelings is an important part of being a responsible person. We do not have the right to feel "good" all the time. We do not have the right to put lives at risk. The question, "What do I feel?" is about identifying what felt "good" about driving impaired and what uncomfortable feelings driving impaired helped us avoid, so that we can then create a plan on how to deal with such feelings when they surface again.

What is Going on in the Moment?

When we identify our beliefs and feelings, we can then deconstruct the moment we made the choices to drive impaired. Think of it as a chain that begins with a belief, which then connects to a set of circumstances, then to a thought and a feeling, and then to a choice to drive impaired An example of this process, *choice chain*, could be:

"I need people to like me to have a sense of self-value. I am out with a group of friends. Everyone is not happy, what did I do wrong? I feel anxious. I can drink alcohol and these feelings will disappear."

This *choice chain* is helpful in assisting a person to understand his/her drinking patterns. While these revelations are important, we ask that you do the additional work of expanding this chain to include the choice to drive impaired. For example, the *choice chain* now could look like:

"I don't believe I am the type of person who could cause an impaired driving collision. I have been drinking all night, and now the bar is closed. I will be fine. I drove drunk before and nothing happened. I am going to drive home."

Developing both of these *choice chains* allows us to see the various steps we took before we made the last choice to impaired driving. In seeing these steps, we create opportunities to re-assess our beliefs and to develop strategies on how to deal with these circumstances when they appear again.

What is Stopping my Change?

It is a simple question, but simple does not mean easy. To explain what we mean by this statement, we will consider a couple of scenarios: For a person who has a substance abuse problem, it would be easy for us to say the solution is to simply "stop using drugs." That was easy, right? Just stop using drugs and your life will improve. Similarly, if we met a person who has accumulated too much debt, we could say that this person should "stop spending so much money." So, what is stopping either person from changing? We have discovered that instilling change in a person's life is never simple. As easy as it may be to identify the things that need to be changed, the struggle comes when we try to implement these changes into our lives.

If we are doing the work to produce personal growth, we should have a good idea of what "things" need to change in our lives. The question remains; "What is stopping us from changing them?" We all have different reasons for delaying our change. These changes are not just "things". These things may be a relationship, a lifestyle, or a way of seeing yourself. Sometimes we may not be willing to let these "things" go. We live with these things. They make us feel good and help us cope with situations that otherwise seem unmanageable.

If you do not know how to deal with a relationship without alcohol/drugs, if you don't know how to stand up to your friends, if you do not think "it" can happen to you, if you do not think change is worth your time; then just admit it. With such an admission, these "things" can begin to look and sound different. We can begin to understand why our change, which may feel difficult to accomplish, is nonetheless essential and urgent. Our group is here to help you overcome these obstacles, not to judge you for them.

Questions:

1. What do you believe? (Review your answers from the "Relationship with Alcohol, Drugs, and Impaired Driving" lesson and then write down your beliefs about your substance use and your choice to impaired driving.)

_____
_____
_____
_____
_____
_____
_____
_____

2. What are you feeling?

_____
_____
_____
_____
_____
_____
_____

3. What is going on in the moment (i.e., describe your *choice chain*)?

_____
_____
_____
_____
_____
_____
_____
_____

4. What is stopping your change?

_____
_____
_____
_____
_____
_____
_____
_____

LESSON 5: "IS IT SAFE FOR ME TO DRINK AGAIN?"

Alcohol is the third-leading cause of preventable death in the United States (Mokdad n. pag.).

"Chapters of My Life"

Chapter 1: I walk down the street. There is a deep hole in the sidewalk. I fall in. I am lost... I am helpless...It wasn't my fault. It takes forever to find a way out.

Chapter 2: I walked down the same street. There is a deep hole in the sidewalk. I pretend that I don't see it. I fall in again. I can't believe that I am in the same place again, but it's not my fault. It still takes a long time to get out.

Chapter 3: I walked down the same street. There is a deep hole in the sidewalk. I see it is there. I still fall in... it is a habit. My eyes are open. I know where I am. It is my fault. I get out immediately.

Chapter 4: I walked down the same street. There is a deep hole in the sidewalk. I walk around it. I don't fall in the hole.

Chapter 5: I chose to walk down another street.
Portia Nelson

• • •

Drinking alcohol demands that one is responsible with his/her decision-making. Driving impaired is a choice that cannot be taken back. We, at **Responsibly Driven**, believe in abstinence; however, we also understand that many people can and do drink alcohol responsibly[5]. Ultimately, you must make the choice between abstinence and responsible drinking. We cannot make it for you. However, before you make this choice, we ask that you take an honest look at yourself, your underlying issues, and all of the actual and potential consequences that came from your substance use. Issues of addiction and substance abuse can be treated, but those individuals with long-term dependency issues should not expect to be able to practice "controlled drinking."

Can I Drink Responsibly?

Responsible drinking is the consumption of alcohol in a safe way that does not put your health or the lives of others at risk. This can be done if you are mindful of the amount of alco-

---

[6] **Responsibly Driven** does not endorse the notion of "using responsibly". Nevertheless, **RD** firmly believes that our perspectives and tools will assist individuals in adopting responsible habits in states where drug use is legalized or who possess legal medical prescriptions.

hol you drink, have a plan on how to end the night (e.g., designating a sober driver, using a cab, or calling a driving service), and are aware of the potential short- and long-term psychological, emotional, and physical risks. However, even with this knowledge, it may be inappropriate for you to drink alcohol.

If you…

>have substance dependency issues,
>
>have a history of impaired driving (regardless of whether you were caught),
>
>have hurt another person (including yourself) while intoxicated, or
>
>have not addressed your underlying issues;
>
>then it is **not safe** for you to attempt to drink alcohol responsibly.

Long-term studies have shown that people with alcohol problems rarely become responsible drinkers (Mooney 153). More than likely, your first drink of alcohol will be the first of many mistakes until you hit "rock bottom." Give yourself a break, stop drinking alcohol, and move on with your life – a life that will be more enjoyable and safer without the inherent risks of alcohol use.

Will Abstinence Work for Me?

Abstinence is the voluntary cessation from the use of narcotics or alcohol. Those who practice abstinence as a lifestyle should be prepared to make substantial changes in their behavior and mindset relative to the use of those substances. This lifestyle change does not mean that your life will be diminished. On the contrary, abstinence from the use of mind-altering substances can increase both the quality and length of your life. The only things you lose from the practice of abstinence are hangovers, health risks, and the potential harm you could inflict on yourself or others while intoxicated.

Your mindset will control your success. Coerced sobriety does not work. A bitter resentment develops in those individuals who feel they have been pushed into sobriety "against their will" (152). Begin to think of abstinence as an opportunity. Instead of "I can't drink anymore!" adopt the mindset of "I get to be sober." In sobriety, we get the opportunity to be dependable, trustworthy, and safe. Be open to these opportunities and the positive changes abstinence can bring to your life.

Abstinence and Recovery

We often use alcohol/drugs to self-treat medical issues, to help us cope with present situations, or to act in accordance with our distorted beliefs. Abstinence without recovery is doomed to fail. We use these substances because they "worked" to manage our issues, at least temporarily. Recovery is about finding new healthy ways of dealing with our past, present, and future. Planning for our sobriety is about identifying and addressing our underlying issues. This may mean getting the medical treatment we have put off, forgiving a person who wronged us, replacing our distorted beliefs, and/or finding new healthier ways of dealing with stressful situations.

Many of us hit a wall at this point. Recognizing the need for change is one thing, embracing change in our lives is another thing. Often this difficulty stems from distorted beliefs we hold. Thoughts such as "Drinking will make this situation better," "It is okay to drink and drive, everybody does it," or "I am not hurting anyone," do not disappear simply because we stopped drinking alcohol/using drugs. **Responsibly Driven** looks to support individuals in uncovering and addressing the issues with substance abuse and impaired driving; however, it is up to the individual to do the internal work to gain sobriety. In sobriety, we regain balance and purpose in our lives. In sobriety, we will regain our ability to be a **Responsibly Driven** person.

Questions

1. Will you choose to abstain from or to responsibly drink alcohol? Explain your choice.

_____
_____
_____
_____
_____
_____
_____
_____

2. If you answered, "responsibly drink alcohol," why have you not drank alcohol responsibly in the past? What has changed?

_____
_____
_____
_____
_____
_____
_____
_____

3. If you answered, "to abstain," What will your life look like sober?

_____
_____
_____
_____
_____
_____
_____

4. What internal and external work is needed for abstinence to become a natural part of your life?

_____
_____
_____
_____
_____
_____
_____
_____

LESSON 6: PERSONAL SOBRIETY

According to a 2018 SAMHSA survey, an estimated 53.2 million people, aged 12 or older, used illicit drug in the past year, which corresponds to 19.4 percent of the population (SAMHSA, 2018 13). . . . Approximately only 3.7 million people, aged 12 or older, received any substance use treatment (51).

You cannot solve a problem from the same consciousness that created it.
You must learn to see the world anew.
Albert Einstein

• • •

Sobriety is more than just an approach to impaired driving. Sobriety is a lifestyle. It is an attitude and a way of life that touches every part of our lives. With this in mind, we must plan for our sobriety by considering both our substance dependency (if any) and the underlying issues that contributed to our destructive behaviors. This approach will help us construct a lasting sobriety—one that directly addresses our underlying issues by allowing each of us to tailor a plan to fit our personal needs. Dr. David Kipper explains this comprehensive view of sobriety in his book, *The Addiction Solution*:

Sobriety is a goal, not a strict definition.

Too much emphasis is placed on a single, cookie-cutter characterization of sobriety as complete abstinence from all drugs and alcohol. This view is so inflexible that is it is often counterproductive. Abstinence works for some people, but it's not a panacea [cure or remedy] *for addiction…*

Complete abstinence doesn't address the root addiction: the primary biochemical imbalance, and unless medical professionals and patients address the primary illness, they leave the door open for other self-destructive [and even addictive] *behaviors: gambling, sex, eating disorders, and many others. So, you wind up with "sober" but depressed alcoholics who still can't get their act together or "clean" but self-loathing drug addicts on the verge of suicide because they can't take any more pain and depression.*

Sobriety must be approached as multidimensional concept of positive and real possibilities that aids each addict's unique circumstance and overall wellness. This personalized and evolving approach moves forward, one attainable step after another, reaching one level [or concept] *of sobriety while seeking to attain another level of wellness. It sets a plan to keep isolated relapses from spiraling the recovering addict to failure or self-defeat.*

The new addiction medicine paradigm goes beyond "clean and sober" to help addicts achieve, nourish, and nurture their overall states of wellness.

So…what is sobriety? Just this: clean, sober…, and well (Kipper 74).

Dr. Kipper's definition of sobriety helps to demonstrate that destructive behaviors (e.g., impaired driving, substance abuse, dependency, etc.) run deeper than we may realize. To get to the root of the problem, we must create a sobriety plan that sufficiently addresses our underlying issues. For example, if an individual uses alcohol and/or drugs to manage stress, it is not enough for him/her to say, "I will stop drinking/using." Drinking alcohol/using drugs is this person's coping mechanism. Because of this habituation when he/she experiences stress, he/she also experiences a proportional urge to drink alcohol/use drugs. Urges lead to relapse while impaired driving leads to death.

In order for this person to be successful in sobriety, his/her sobriety plan must include the development of coping mechanisms that help him/her safely deal with stress. Similarly, if a person holds beliefs that "everybody drinks and drives," or that "buzzed driving is no big deal," then he/she must come to an understanding that these beliefs are untrue. In his/her plan, he/she will have to take the additional step of accepting the truth—that driving while impaired is dangerous to human life and under no condition should be practiced. The bottom line is that we must find a solution for each of these problems.

CS3 Sobriety Plan Introduction

In this lesson, we will begin the work of creating personal sobriety plans. In the last group session, each participant will present his/her *CS3 Sobriety Plan* to the group (refer to Appendix A – *CS3 Sobriety Plan* Template). The plan will encompass your definition of sobriety, your underlying issues, and how you intend to address them. If you choose to drink alcohol, then you must explain how you can do so in a responsible way that does not put lives at risk. If you choose to abstain from alcohol, you will have to explain how you will maintain your abstinence.

In **Responsibly Driven**, we believe each person's sobriety plan must demonstrate the following four components:

CLEAN: I will abstain from behaviors that could be harmful to my health.

SOBER: I will avoid actions that adversely impair my judgment. Above all, I will strive to maintain a clear mind.

SAFE: I will avoid actions that could put my life or the lives of others at risk.

SUSTAINABLE: I will work to maintain long-term sobriety that is a natural part of my life.

As a group, we will be looking to see if your plan sufficiently fulfills each of these components—Is your plan *clean, safe, sober,* and *sustainable*? Our goal is life-long sobriety. Impaired driving cannot be a possibility in our futures. We can never again put ourselves in situations that endanger our lives and the lives of others.

Ultimately, the choice and responsibility are yours. The purpose of this open account is for you to come up with a realistic and durable plan for your sobriety and to receive honest feedback from your fellow group members. We are not looking for the "right" answer. We are looking for your "right" answer. One that is *clean, sober, safe,* and *sustainable.*

Questions

1. Define your concept of sobriety.

_____

_____

_____

_____

_____

_____

_____

2. Define the *CS3 Sobriety Plan's* four components: *clean, sober, safe,* and *sustainable.*

_____

_____

_____

_____

_____

_____

_____

Begin to work on your *CS3 Sobriety Plan* (Appendix A). You can use the *CS3 Sobriety Plan* template to record your answers from the above listed questions. We suggest that you use pencil, so you can edit your plan neatly as you gain new insight.

LESSON 7: FROM THE IMPAIRED DRIVING SURVIVOR'S PERSPECTIVE

One person is killed from an impaired driving auto collision every twenty minutes in the United States (National Highway Traffic Safety Administration, *Overview*). *Every two minutes, a person is injured in a drunk driving crash* (MADD).

We think we listen, but very rarely do we listen with real understanding, true empathy. Yet listening, of this very special kind, is one of the most potent forces for change that I know.
Carl Rogers

• • •

Impaired driving produces victims and survivors, like any other type of crime. The difference between a victim and a survivor is that a victim is tragically killed by the impaired driving collision, whereas a survivor remains alive (or is functioning as a business/organization), but may endure a range of consequences stemming from the impaired driving auto collision.

In this lesson, we will be examining three components that are key to understanding the victim/survivor experience: *Three Levels of Victimization, Four Areas of Impact,* and *Five Elements of the Recovery Process*. By learning about these components, we can begin to comprehend the magnitude that our actions have on ourselves and others. Without such an understanding, it is far too easy to dismiss our irresponsible behavior of impaired driving.

Three Levels of Victimization

There are three different levels of victimization: primary, secondary, and tertiary. Those individuals who are directly involved in or witness the impaired driving incident are called primary victims. Such individuals are motorists and/or pedestrians hit by an impaired driver. The impaired driver's passengers are also considered primary victims. Secondary victims are not directly involved in the impaired driving incident, but still bear much of the effects caused by the auto collision. First responders who respond to the auto collision caused by the impaired driver, along with the victim's loved ones, are classified as secondary victims. As the news about the collision spreads, another category of victims is created, tertiary victims. Tertiary victims include, but are not limited to, the victim's extended family members and social circle, criminal justice officials, counselors, funeral directors, insurance agents, news reporters, and community members.

Some may call this phenomenon the "Ripple Effect", but in reality, there is nothing small about impaired driving and its consequences on human lives. Impaired driving's impact is far-reaching and long-lasting. The "Ripple Effect" devastates impaired driving victims' and survivors' lives, therefore, it is more accurate for impaired driving to be described as a massive tidal wave.

Our behaviors impact a wide range of persons. Regardless of their level of victimization, their lives have been irreversibly altered by our irresponsible actions. This is a sobering revelation. If our reckless decision to drive impaired can adversely affect people-close and distant, then choosing to act in a prosocial manner can transform people and their lives.

Four Areas of Impact

There are four areas to consider when identifying the impact of impaired driving: physical, emotional, financial, and spiritual (US Department of Justice, *Victim Impact: Listen and Learn*, 10-11). We seek to clarify the impact of our behavior to assist us in developing empathy towards our victims and survivors and to ascertain the types of amends we need to make to them. As you read this next section, reflect on your past behaviors and their effect on the four different areas of impact.

Physical

Physical ailments can arise immediately or long after an auto collision. Some examples of physical ailments are broken bones, bruises, concussions, lacerations, headaches, back pain, weight gain or loss, lack of energy, and difficult breathing. Physical ailments may impair a survivor's ability to be productive and effective in his/her life. Case in point, a construction worker who suffers a back injury may no longer be able to work on a construction site. A mother who experiences daily headaches and a lack of energy may not engage with her family as much as she did prior to the impaired driving auto collision.

Physical injuries place great strain on individuals and families. Imagine having one of your physical abilities inhibited or taken from you. How would that reduce your ability or impact your daily interactions? How would it impede your freedom? How would this change of life make you feel?

Emotional

Emotional changes develop after all auto collisions, but they are intensified when the collision involves an impaired driver. A person who is involved in a collision with an impaired driver experiences a range of emotions, frequencies, and intensities. Some examples of emotional responses are hypervigilance; sadness; grief; escalated fear and anxiety; and increased stress, anger, and frustration. An impaired driving survivor who is experiencing an escalated state of fear and anxiety towards driving may not be able to visit his/her family and friends or continue working at his/her job. An impaired driving survivor may also succumb to grief and sadness over the traumatic experience and may be crippled by the onset of depression.

In our experience, negative emotional changes greatly reduce a person's motivation to live. A diminished level of enthusiasm creates the likelihood that a person will experience a lower level of personal and professional engagement. Consider your past experiences with uncomfortable emotional states. Did you possess the necessary drive to be fully engaged with your family, friends, or professional peers? Did you retain the required level of zest to enjoy your relationships and life? Impaired driving creates a horrific emotional disruption in the lives of survivors. Our hope is that by recognizing the horrendous impact impaired driving has on people's emotional states, it will compel you to reconsider your daily decisions.

Financial

Financial losses accrue after an impaired driving collision. A common misbelief is that a person's car insurance policy covers the cost of an auto collision; unfortunately, this belief is not true. Many drivers' policies are limited in coverage and/or the drivers may not be able to pay the deductibles. In addition, impaired drivers far too often do not have car insurance or even possess a valid Driver's License. The following are examples of financial losses: car repairs or replacement, insurance deductibles, salary loss, burial expenses, and replacement of damaged items. All financial losses have the potential to diminish a person's livelihood. An impaired driving survivor may no longer be able to take his/her family on vacation because he/she must now buy a new car. Another impaired driving survivor may have to take out a loan to pay for his/her child's funeral.

The sad reality of our society is that most Americans are living paycheck to paycheck, with less than $400 in their savings account. Any sort of setback, minor or large, can fundamentally reshape a person's or family's future. Even for our fellow community members who are financially blessed, impaired driving can drastically change their way of life. If the person who contributes most of the money in the family is severely injured or killed, that family's lifestyle will be considerably changed. We encourage you to review your financial state and to consider how different your life would be if you were burdened by the financial strain of an impaired driving collision.

Spiritual

Crime fundamentally alters a survivor's worldview. Being involved in an impaired driving incident is not different. Impaired driving survivors may struggle to answer the big "Why" question as they attempt to regain some semblance of normalcy, power, and control in their lives. Survivors will contemplate questions about their humanity, sense of goodness, and religious tenets of forgiveness, retaliation, and punishment. We will examine the spiritual area of impact more in the following section.

Five Elements of the Recovery Process

In order to facilitate the recovery process and heal their spiritual wounds, crime survivors seek to reestablish their sense of safety and personal empowerment, to gain restitution and an apology from the impaired driver, and to answer the "Six Basic Questions of Healing" (Zehr 27).

Safety

A person's sense of safety is composed of one's belief that "the world is an orderly, meaningful place and belief of personal autonomy" (Zehr 24- 25). Impaired driving rattles this understanding. People tend to believe that as long as they are obeying the law, they will be secure while they are in their vehicle. They also expect that others will obey the laws. Personal autonomy entails the belief that one possesses power over one's own life. Impaired driving shatters this belief as well. Imagine enjoying a leisurely walk or drive while entertaining a conversation with a relative or friend. A person expects to be able finish those conversations and to be able return home safely. How would your sense of safety be affected if suddenly an impaired driver crashed into your life?

Empowerment

The process of empowerment is extremely important in order to overcome a traumatic event. With growth and maturity, we develop confidence in our abilities and relationships, but when we encounter a traumatic event, that confidence wavers. Doubt sets in and creates massive confusion regarding what we can and cannot accomplish and who we can and cannot trust. For survivors, this sense of inferiority and insecurity can be painfully debilitating.

Empowerment reestablishes one's confidence in his/her efficacy and effectiveness. Empowerment provides survivors with a foundation to reconstruct their relationships and futures. Survivors of impaired driving can become empowered by talking about experiences with others. Through the process of sharing, impaired driving survivors identify commonalities with other survivors and inform other people how to prevent future impaired driving collisions. Survivors regain a sense of ownership over their lives as they begin to feel empowered.

Restitution

Impaired driving causes immense financial loss. A part of the recovery process is having the impaired driver accept responsibility for his/her decisions and its adverse effects that are imposed on the survivor. Restitution–the act of compensating loss, damage, or injury–is a key aspect of being accountable. Moreover, restitution significantly assists survivors reconstruct their lives after such a traumatic event.

Restitution does not erase the pain and damage of an impaired driving auto collision. When an impaired driver fulfills his/her obligation of restitution, he/she communicates to the survivors an acknowledgment of responsibility and contrition. Think of past times when someone damaged or lost something valuable to you. Compare the different experiences you had when the responsible person replaced or fixed that item versus the time when the responsible person did not replace or fix that item; there is a significant difference. The fulfillment of restitution can completely transform a way a survivor experiences a traumatic event such as impaired driving.

Apology

An impaired driving collision is NOT an accident. It is the result of a series of conscious decisions to break the law; consequently, an innocent person(s) was hurt or killed. Therefore, the impaired driver owes an authentic apology to his/her victim(s) and survivor(s). Victims and survivors are entitled to a genuine expression of contrition. Consider the agonizing amount of energy and time a survivor may ponder if his/her assailant even acknowledges the harm caused. Without such a remorseful declaration, survivors may experience ongoing trauma. An apology is a sign of sincerity and humility because it demonstrates to survivors a recognition of responsibility and a willingness to make amends.

Let us consider how to compose and deliver an apology. Ohio State University researchers conducted two separate experiments on apologies (Grabmeier n. pag.). They identified six major components of a successful apology: an expression of regret, an explanation of what went wrong, an acknowledgement of responsibility, a declaration of repentance, an offer of repair, and a request for forgiveness. An impaired driver must be able to account for his/her irresponsible decisions. Being able to acknowledge his/her responsibility in each of these components is essential to assisting the healing process of the survivor's and victim's family, along with his/her own personal growth.

Need for Answers

Survivors ponder many questions after the impaired driving auto collision. Being able to satisfactorily address the "Six Basic Questions of Healing" will help facilitate the healing process (Zehr 27):

1. What happened?
2. Why did it happen to me?
3. Why did I act as I did at that time?
4. Why have I acted as I have since that time?
5. What if it happens again?
6. What does this mean to me and for my outlook, my faith, my worldview, my future, etc.?

These sorts of questions are difficult for any type of situation. Impaired driving auto collisions only heighten the insecurity and confusion that a survivor possesses. The experience of the said event can seem very random, thus creating a sense of perplexity. The quest for the answers to the above listed questions helps survivors link the pieces of their shattered worldview back together. Some survivors are able to discover the answers to their questions while others are plagued by uncertainty.

Questions

1. Who is affected by your decision to drink alcohol/using drugs and drive impaired?

_____
_____
_____
_____
_____
_____
_____

2. How is each area of impact affected by impaired driving?

_____
_____
_____
_____
_____
_____
_____

3. Can an impaired driving survivor live a fulfilling life without obtaining the *Five Elements of the Recovery Process*? Why or why not?

_____
_____
_____
_____
_____

LESSON 8: THE CONSEQUENCES OF IMPAIRED DRIVING

Every two minutes, a person is injured in a drunk driving crash…Drunk driving costs each adult in the United States over $500 per year (MADD).

Empathy is allowing someone else's pain into your heart.
Jim Micheletti

• • •

Cost of Impaired Driving

In 2018, 10,511 people died in alcohol-impaired auto collisions (US Depart. of Transportation, *Traffic Safety Facts 2018, 1*). Those are the numbers. What cannot be measured is the overwhelming sense of grief and loss experienced by impaired driving victims' and their loved ones—a mother who receives the heartbreaking news that her son/daughter was killed, a father struggling to explain to his children why their mother will not be coming home, and a child forced to grow up without parents. Because of one person's choice to drive while intoxicated, lives are irreparably damaged.

We must also remember the DUI survivors, those who live with psychological and physical pain and disability. These once healthy individuals now suffer with issues of pain management, paralysis, and/or traumatic brain injury after being struck by an individual driving impaired. How much is someone's health worth? How can these survivors ever be compensated for their losses?

Guided Meditation Exercise

To help us gain some insight into the consequences of impaired driving, we ask that you participate in a guided meditation exercise.

Instructions:

This is a guided visualization exercise. Relax and listen to the suggestions offered. Allow your imagination to be as detailed as possible during this exercise. Even if you have no idea what an impaired driving survivor might experience, allow your imagination to guide you into an understanding.

Imagine you are driving one night. You are in your car, moving steadily down the highway. Think of where you are going? (Pause) *Is anyone with you?* (Pause) *What are your plans for the night?* (Pause) *How do you feel?* (Long Pause)

Then suddenly, it happens! Your only warning is the sound of tires screeching as another driver veers into your lane, smashing directly into your car. The immediate impact thrusts your whole body forward into the steering wheel. The violent collision tosses your car to the side as twisting metal and broken glass fill the air. Finally, your car comes to a stop. You are pinned within the wreckage, desperately fighting to remain conscious. What is happening? (Pause) *What thoughts are running through your mind?* (Pause) *What type of physical pain are you experiencing?* (Pause) *Is anyone else hurt?* (Pause) *How much time lapses before help arrives?* (Pause) *What are your fears?* (Long Pause)

You wake up in the hospital as the medical staff informs you that the driver of the other car are the only survivors. They go on to say that your injuries are severe and that there is a possibility that you may never walk again. How do you react to the news? (Pause) *What emotions and feelings are running through your mind?* (Pause) *How will a disability affect your life* (Pause), *your job,* (Pause), *your relationships,* (Pause) *your future plans and dreams?* (Long Pause)

A few hours later, two police officers enter the room. They inform you that the driver who struck your car was intoxicated. What is your reaction? (Pause) *How do you feel about the driver?* (Pause) *What do you want to say to him/her?* (Pause for an extended period to allow the participant to reflect.)

Exercise Process

You went through the guided meditation exercise that attempts to convey the real-life consequences of impaired driving as experienced by a survivor. Consider the following questions: How was that experience? What thoughts came up? What emotions were you experiencing as you imagined those experiences? What questions would you want to ask the impaired driver?

Now imagine yourself as the impaired driver. How would you answer these questions? Why did you choose to drive impaired? What were you thinking? What was more important than obeying the law or more important than yours and the public's safety?

Testimonials from Impaired Driving Survivors[7]

As you are aware, the brief guided meditation exercise only offers a glimpse into the mind of an impaired driving survivor. The instructor will now read some excerpts from real survivors and other individuals impacted by impaired driving. Keep in mind your reaction to the imagined impaired driving collision as you hear their accounts.

<u>A Former EMT/Paramedic</u>

I resigned from my career and started experiencing health issues. I was diagnosed with bi-polar disorder. It wasn't until twenty years later that I discovered that I was not bi-polar, but suffered from Post-Traumatic Stress Disorder (PTSD). The nightmares had taken a

---

[7] Testimonial excerpts are from the testimonial book, *IMPACT: Insights, Effects and the Reality of Impaired Driving.*

toll on me. I would love to be a paramedic again, but with PTSD, I don't think I could do it. I lost too many patients (Responsibly Drive DUI Project 57).

A Family Insurance Agent

I'm sitting in front of two very kind people. I don't know them. I have never met them and my stomach is in knots. Something isn't right. This is not a conversation I want to be having. They aren't even my clients. He begins to talk, and I become nauseous. I feel raw. I want to fix this for them, but nothing can be done (39).

A Mother of an Impaired Driver

(He) was in critical condition, suffering from severe traumatic brain injury with multiple life-threatening injuries…He was on death's door…Staff told us that they didn't think he was going to live, and if he did, he would be a vegetable. I was struck with fear and sadness…If (he) did survive, would he go to jail for manslaughter…Months later (he) came out of his coma…Realizing (he) would need daily therapy, (my family) built an extensive, fully-equipped and staffed neurological rehabilitation clinic…[T]he financial hardship that has been placed our family is never-ending (22-26).

An Impaired Driving Survivor

[F]orty-four years after the fatal car crash that took my family, [m]any friends and family still miss my [family]. Would my twins still look alike if they were alive? I was never able to see my daughters go to school, graduate high school or go to college. I never experienced their falling in love, getting married or having babies of their own. I love them and miss them every day. My husband and I didn't get to live our lives together and celebrate what would be our fiftieth wedding anniversary. All because of a drunk driver. Who knows if one of our daughters would have become president or done something phenomenal for the world? A drunk driver took these answers away from me (73).

Impaired driving reaches all facets of society. Its devastation creates deep wounds that people carry throughout their lives and into their relationships. These excerpts only present a glimmer of their pain and agony. As you sit in the group discussions, use these survivors' words to build empathic insight.

Questions

1. Describe your experience–feelings and thoughts–from the guided meditation exercise.

_____

_____

_____

2. What aspect(s) of the impaired driving survivors' testimonials stood out the most, and why?
___
___
___
___
___
___
___

3. How was your experience of the guided meditation exercise different from hearing the experiences from actual impaired driving survivors?
___
___
___
___
___
___
___

4. How has this experience affected your view about your past choices to drive impaired?
___
___
___
___
___
___
___

5. How will this experience influence your future choice to drive impaired?
___
___
___

LESSON 9: CS3 SOBRIETY PLAN PREPARATION

A study from the Dominican University in California on goal setting with nearly 270 participants found that you are 42 percent more likely to achieve your goals if you write them down (Economy).

The future depends on what we do with the present.
Mohandas K. Gandhi

• • •

Now that we have completed the previous nine lessons, we are ready to put the finishing touches on our *CS3 Sobriety Plans* (Refer to Appendix A – *CS3 Sobriety Plan* Template). As we have emphasized throughout the program, your sobriety must fulfill the following requirements. It must be:

CLEAN: I will abstain from behaviors that could be harmful to my health.

SOBER: I will avoid actions that adversely impair my judgment. Above all, I will strive to maintain a clear mind.

SAFE: I will avoid actions that could put my life or the lives of others at risk.

SUSTAINABLE: I will work to maintain long-term sobriety that is a natural part of my life.

In order to meet this standard, it is essential that you be able to finish these statements completely:

- *"My problem is...* [State what specific circumstance(s) led you to this program (i.e., multiple DUI arrests, impaired driving auto collisions, substance abuse, etc.).]
- *"The underlying issues(s) that led to my problem(s) are..."* [List your underlying issue(s), and then explain how it has led to the formation of your distorted thought(s) and belief(s).]
- *"The underlying issue(s) led to my destructive behavior because..."* [Connect the dots between your underlying issue(s), distorted belief(s), and your destructive behavior (i.e., your substance abuse, impaired driving, etc.).]
- *"I will address my underlying issue(s) by..."* [Explain how you are addressing the underlying issue(s) of your destructive behavior (e.g., replacing your distort belief(s) with what is really true, forgiving a family member, AA participation, etc.).]

You will also need to be able to answer these following questions:

"What elements of your *CS3 Sobriety Plan* support the requirement of being..."

Clean?
_____
_____
_____

Sober?
_____
_____
_____

Safe?
_____
_____
_____

Sustainable?
_____
_____
_____

Finish your *CS3 Sobriety Plan* by answering the above listed questions. You can use the *CS3 Sobriety Plan* template to record your answers. We still suggest that you use pencil, so you edit your plan neatly as you gain new insight.

LESSON 10: CS3 SOBRIETY PLAN PRESENTATIONS

One of the earliest studies on influence found that feedback in the form of short comments, rather than grades alone, significantly improved performance (Page n. pag.).

In the time of your life, live.
William Saroyan

• • •

You have completed all the previous lessons and should now be fully prepared to give an open personal account of your *CS3 Sobriety Plan*. Before presenting your plan, we should first lay out some general ground rules for both the presenters and group members to have the same understanding of the *CS3 Sobriety Plan's* purpose and goals.

Presentation of CS3 Plans

<u>For Presenters</u>

- In your statement, you should answer all the questions posed in the previous sections: What is my problem(s) and underlying issue(s)? How I will address them? How is my sobriety plan *clean, sober, safe,* and *sustainable*?

- You will be responsible to give an honest account of yourself and to describe a plan that is realistic and achievable.

- You should be prepared to answer questions from your fellow group members and facilitators as to whether your sobriety plan fulfills the requirements of being *clean, safe, sober,* and *sustainable*.

- Be honest. If you do not know the answer, say so. It took some time to get to where you are, so it may take some time to find your way out. It is better to say that you are working towards the solution while in sobriety than misrepresenting yourself. You do not have to be perfect to be sober. Nevertheless, if there is an essential ingredient to sobriety, it is honesty.

- Be courageous by being willing to hear another person's experience of you and to face things that may be unflattering.

- Be humble by acknowledging your humanity. We are all humans and possess blind spots. When these blind spots come up there is a natural reaction to become defensive and to protect our ego and pride. Resist the temptation to defend yourself.

- Be compassionate towards yourself. You have taken many positive steps to get this far. You are doing great!

For Group Members

- Keep your questions centered on the four components: *clean, sober, safe,* and *sustainable.*
- We will be giving non-aversive feedback. In other words, if you disagree with someone's sobriety plan, find a way to express that disagreement in a constructive manner.
- Offer your feedback from a posture of caring. Remember we are here to support each other. Always keep that purpose in mind.
- Remember this is not your account. We are to evaluate the individual, their problems, and their solutions. Do not confuse their sobriety plan with your own. Not everyone has your problems, so your solutions may not work for someone else.
- Be supportive and critical. If you have a positive remark, please voice it. Sometimes the best motivation to maintain our sobriety is the positive recognition of our peers. Therefore, if you have seen one of your fellow group members make progress in their sobriety, now is the best time to acknowledge it.

Closing

Congratulations! You have completed **Responsibly Driven's** *An Impaired Driving Prevention Curriculum.* This has been a long and arduous process. Honest introspection is a grueling process because it requires us to be open about the things we have tried so desperately to hide. It demands that one develops a clear moral compass to ensure that he/she makes decisions that align with his/her future vision. You should be proud of yourself for being courageous and embarking on such a humbling and transformative journey.

Responsibly Driven has seen remarkable success with those individuals who challenge their past assumptions about substance use and other self-destructive behaviors. You have the strength and the ability to adopt empowering perspectives to influence the change you dream to embody. If you follow your *CS3 Sobriety Plan,* rest assured you will step into the vision you have casted for yourself.

ACKNOWLEDGMENTS

Without their generous contributions of time, wisdom, and love in this effort, this project would have never come to fruition. We would like to thank the following individuals:

The founding members of **Responsibly Driven:** Thank you for your commitment to impaired driving prevention. Thank you for this redemptive journey, in which we shared many tears, laughs, and insights. Your efforts will transform the impaired driving conversation.

Roberta Schweers, Connie McGeorgy, Sandra Wise, and other CDCR staff sponsors: Thank you for all the support that you have given **Responsibly Driven** over the years. Without your trust, we would have never been able to accomplish so many of our goals.

Jesse Bonderman: Thank you for patience and honesty during our intensive workshops. Your authentic feedback provided the group with so much valuable insight. We have utilized your perspectives in hopes of discovering true contrition and responsibility.

Julie Castro: Thank you for your faith in **Responsibly Driven**. Since you have joined our team, we have been able to spread our message to the general public in ways we never thought was possible.

Our Families: Thank you for your love and support throughout the years. We are eternally indebted to you. We seek to honor your sacrifice by becoming the men you know that we can become.

Impaired Driving Victims and Survivors: We can never say, "Sorry," enough times. The men of **Responsibly Driven** strive to honor you by rebuilding the communities that we have destroyed and by preventing another family from enduring the devastating pain and anguish that we have unjustly inflicted on you.

BIBLIOGRAPHY

Aaronson, Elliot and Carol Tavris. *Mistakes Were Made (But Not by Me)*. San Diego: Harcourt, 2007. Print.

Adult Children of Alcoholics (Association). *The 12 Steps for Adult Children*. San Diego: Recovery Publications, 1987. Print.

BACTrack. "DUI Statistics". *BACTrack*. N.d. Web. 13 Oct. 2020. <https://www.bactrack.com/blogs/expert-center/35040645-dui-statistics>.

Bell, Lindsay. "4 Listening Styles Communicators Should Know." *Ragan's PR Daily*. Ragan Communications, Inc. 21 Nov. 2013. Web. 12 Dec. 2019. <https://www.prdaily.com/4-listening-styles-communicators-should-know/>.

Center for Wellness Promotion. "Progressive Effects of Alcohol Consumption". *UNC Charlotte*. N.d. Web. 30 Dec. 2019. <https://wellness.uncc.edu/sites/wellness.uncc.edu/files/media/Stay%20In%20The%20Green%20BAC.pdf>.

Comer, Ronald S. *Abnormal Psychology*. 4th Ed. New York: Worth Publisher, 2001. Print.

Economy, Peter. "This Is the Way You Need to Write Down Your Goals for Faster Success." *Inc*. N.p. 2 Feb 2018. Web. 29 Oct 2020. <https://www.inc.com/peter-economy/this-is-way-you-need-to-write-down-your-goals-for-faster-success.html>.

Esurance Insurance Services, Inc. "The True Cost of DUI". *Allstate*. 2004. Web. November 2018. <http://www.esurance.com/violations/true-cost-of-dui>.

Golson Jr, William T. *On the Matter of Relationships*. Maitland: Xulon Press, 2007. Print.

Gorski, Terrence T. *Denial Management: Workbook*. Independence: Herald Publishing/Independence Press, 2000. Print.

Grabmeier, Jeff. "The 6 Elements of an Effective Apology, According to Science." *Ohio State News*. 12 April 2016. Web. 27 Dec. 2019. <https://news.osu.edu/the-6-elements-of-an-effective-apology-according-to-science/>.

Henslin, James M. *Essential of Sociology: A Down-to-Earth Approach*. 5th Ed. San Francisco: Pearson, 2004. Print.

Kipper, David and Steven Whitney. *The Addiction Solution*. New York: Rodal Inc. 2010. Print.

Lomurro, Munson, Comer, Brown & Schottland, LLC. "Percent of Convicted of Drunk

Drivers Who Were Repeat Offenders". *Lomurro Law Trial Lawyers*. 26 Feb 2018. Web. 13 Oct. 2020. <https://www.lomurrolaw.com/percent-of-drunk-drivers-who-were-repeat-offenders/>.

Mother Against Drunk Driving (MADD). "Statistics". *MADD: No More Victims*. 2020. Web. 13 Oct. 20. <https://www.madd.org/statistics/>.

Mendelson, Jack and Nancy Mello. *The Addictive Personality*. Philadelphia: Chelsea House Publisher, 1978. Print.

Mokdad, A.H., J.S. Marks, D.F. Stroup, and J.L. Gerberding. "Actual Causes of Death in the United States 2000". *Journal of the American Medical Association* 291(10): 1238–1245, 2004. Print.

Mooney, J., A. Eisenberg, and H. Eisenberg. *The Recovery Book*. New York: Workman Publishing, New York, NY, 1992. Print.

Page, E. B. (1958). "Teacher Comments and Student Performance: A Seventy-Four Classroom Experiment In School Motivation". *Journal of Educational Psychology* 49(4), 173–181. Print.

Prentiss, Chris and Pax Prentiss. *The Alcoholism and Addictive Cure*. Los Angeles: Power Press, 2007. Print.

Ray, Oakley S., and Charles Ksir. *Drugs, Society, and Human Behavior*. Boston: McGraw-Hill, 1993. Print.

Responsibly Drive DUI Project. *IMPACT: Insights, Effects and the Reality of Impaired Driving*. Phoenix: Fiesta Publishing, 2018. Print.

Rohr, Richard. *Breathing Under Water: Spirituality and the Twelve Steps*. Cincinnati: Franciscan Media, 2011. Print.

Schumann, Karina and Carol S. Dweck. "Who Accepts Responsibility for Their Transgressions?" *Personality and Social Psychology Bulletin*. Vol 40, Issue 12. 2014. Print.

State of California. Department of Motor Vehicles. *California Driver Handbook*. CA. Gov. N.d. Web. Dec. 2019. <https://www.dmv.ca.gov/portal/dmv/detail/pubs/hdbk/actions_aps_court>.

Substance Abuse and Mental Health Services Administration (SAMHSA). *Key Substance Use and Mental Health Indicators in the United States: Results from the 2015 National Survey on Drug Use and Health*. 2015. Web. 25 Jan. 2017. <https://www.samhsa.gov/data/sites/default/files/NSDUH-FFR1-2015Rev1/NSDUH-FFR1-2015Rev1/NSDUH-FFR1-2015Rev1/NSDUH-National%20Findings-REVISED-2015.pdf>.

---. *Key Substance Use and Mental Health Indicators in the United States: Results from the 2018 National Survey on Drug Use and Health*. 2019. Web. 12 Nov. 2020. <https://www.samhsa.gov/

data/sites/default/files/cbhsq-reports/NSDUHNationalFindingsReport2018/NSDUHNationalFindingsReport2018.pdf>.

---. Center for Behavioral Health Statistics and Quality (CBHSQ). *2014 National Survey on Drug Use and Health: Detailed Tables.* Print. (2015).

United States Department of Justice. National Institute on Alcohol Facts and Alcoholism. *Alcohol Facts and Statistics.* 2020. Web. 11 Nov. 2020. <https://www.niaaa.nih.gov/sites/default/files/publications/NIAAA_Alcohol_FactsandStats_102020.pdf>.

United States Department of Justice. Federal Bureau of Investigation. *Crime in the United States 2016: Uniform Crime Reports.* 2017. Web. 16 April 2018. <https://ucr.fbi.gov/crime-in-the-u.s/2016/crime-in-the-u.s.-2016/tables/table-18>.

---. Federal Bureau of Investigation. *Crime in the United States 2016: Uniform Crime Reports.* 2017. Web. 16 April 2018. <https://ucr.fbi.gov/crime-in-the-u.s/2016/crime-in-the-u.s.-2016/tables/table-18external icon>.

---. Office or Victims of Crime. "Engaging Communities: Empowering Victims". *2015 NCVRW Resource Guide.* Washington, DC: 2015. Print.

---. Office for Victims of Crime. *Victim Impact: Listen Learn: Facilitator Manual.* Washington, DC: GPO, 2009. Print.

United States Department of Transportation. National Highway Traffic Safety Administration (NHTSA). *Overview.* 2020. Web. 9 Sept. 2020. <https://www.nhtsa.gov/risky-driving/drunk-driving#:~:text=In%20fact%2C%20on%20average%20over,year%20in%20drunk%2Ddriving%20crashes>.

---. National Highway Traffic Safety Administration. *Traffic Safety Facts: 2016 Data - Alcohol-Impaired Driving.* 2017. Web. 12 Nov 2020. <https://crashstats.nhtsa.dot.gov/Api/Public/ViewPublication/812450>.

---. National Highway Traffic Safety Administration. *Traffic Safety Facts: 2018 Data - Alcohol-Impaired Driving.* 2019. Web. 12 Nov. 2020. <https://crashstats.nhtsa.dot.gov/Api/Public/ViewPublication/812864>.

---. National Highway Traffic Safety Administration. *Traffic Safety Facts: 2018 Fatal Motor Vehicle Crashes: Overview.* 2019. Web. 7 Oct. 2020. <https://crashstats.nhtsa.dot.gov/Api/Public/ViewPublication/812826>.

Zehr, Howard. *Changing Lenses: A New Focus for Crime and Justice.* Scottsdale: Herald Press, 2005. Print.

APPENDICES

APPENDIX A: CS3 SOBRIETY PLAN
CLEAN, SOBER, SAFE, AND SUSTAINABLE (CS3) SOBRIETY PLAN

Name: _____ **Date:** _____

Your *CS3 Sobriety Plan* must fulfill the following requirements. It must be:

CLEAN: I will abstain from behaviors that could be harmful to my health.

SOBER: I will avoid actions that adversely impair my judgment. Above all, I will strive to maintain a clear mind.

SAFE: I will avoid actions that could put my life or the lives of others at risk.

SUSTAINABLE: I will work to maintain long-term sobriety that is a natural part of my life.

1. *"My problem is..."* [State what specific circumstance(s) led you to this program (i.e., multiple DUI arrests, impaired driving auto collisions, substance abuse, etc.).]

_____
_____
_____
_____
_____
_____
_____

2. *"The underlying issues(s) that led to my problem(s) are..."* [List your underlying issue(s), and then explain how it has led to the formation of your distorted thought(s) and belief(s).]

_____
_____
_____
_____
_____
_____
_____

3. *"The underlying issue(s) led to my destructive behavior because..."* [Connect the dots between your underlying issue(s), distorted belief(s), and your destructive behavior (i.e., your substance abuse, impaired driving, etc.).]

_____
_____
_____
_____
_____
_____
_____

4. *"I will address my underlying issue(s) by..."* [Explain how you are addressing the underlying issue(s) of your destructive behavior (e.g. replacing your distort belief(s) with what is really true, forgiving a family member, AA participation, etc.).]

_____
_____
_____
_____
_____
_____
_____

5. What elements of your *CS3 Sobriety Plan* support the requirement of being . . .?
    CLEAN:

_____
_____
_____
_____
_____
_____
_____

SOBER:

___

SAFE:

___

SUSTAINABLE:

___

MISCELLANEOUS NOTES:

___

APPENDIX B: FACILITATOR'S GUIDE

Responsibly Driven is a program that is centered on life experience. It is through personal experience that facilitators draw their strength, insight, empathy, and purpose. Impaired driving is a destructive behavior that is far too often overlooked in society. People typically minimize or justify the behavior when they are involved; however, the very instance someone else drives impaired judgments are easily issued. The utilization of life experience in a group session is more likely to dismiss participants' denial , such as justifications, rationalizations, minimizations, than theoretical discussions about the dangers of impaired driving. It is our experience that participants are more open to honest introspection when engaged by a person with shared life experiences. **Responsibly Driven** encourages potential facilitators to be courageous and to tap into your vast resource of personal history. As leaders, we must be willing to "go first" in any endeavor that we ask of others. Participants will recognize and appreciate a facilitator's candor and authenticity.

General Tips for Facilitators

In the following section, we will offer some general tips that have found real value for us during group sessions.

Lesson Facilitation

<u>Lesson Format:</u> The lesson format is uniformed to simplify the process of facilitation delivery (except for the <u>Introduction</u> section).

Group Check-In & Chapter Quote: Each lesson begins with a check-in section, because it is important to assess the participants' emotional and mental state and their understanding of the previous lessons. In addition, **Responsibly Driven** encourages facilitators to patiently address pertinent questions and/or concerns in order to avoid potential obstacles. After the check-in portion, we introduce a famous quote to stimulate the participants' interest and thoughts. Each quote is selected for its connection to the lesson's topic and concepts. Allow most of the group members to comment on the quote before revealing its connection to the lesson.

Presentation of Chapter Concepts: At the top of each lesson format is a list of the lesson's key concepts. Briefly introduce these concepts to the group. Throughout the group discussion, facilitators should be vigilant for opportunities to emphasize the lesson's key points.

Group Exercise: In some of the group sessions, we have added an exercise to assist in the presentation of the key concepts. We have found that some insights are easier to develop through experience rather than didactic discussion, and that there is value in breaking the monotony of group sessions.

Group Discussion on Chapter: In this section, facilitators will orchestrate a conversation about the lesson's topics and/or exercise(s). We have listed a series of questions to help stimulate a group discussion; however, our questions are merely suggestions. We encourage facilitators to use their listening skills to identify vital clarifying questions that will steer the group conversation towards the most appropriate destination. Facilitators must be attentive to their group discussions. By doing so, facilitators will be able to emphasize pertinent discoveries particular to the specific conversation.

Landing Points: In this section, the facilitator(s) provides the group with the main takeaway(s) from the lessons, in addition to re-summarizing all the key points and discovered insights that were discussed. The facilitator(s) must ensure that these key points are sufficiently covered before proceeding to the next lesson.

Check-Out: Before the close of lesson, participants are offered an opportunity to share their pressing thoughts. In addition, facilitators are to give participants the lesson's assignments to complete.

Lesson Assignments: Each lesson has a set of questions that the participants are to answer before the next lesson. Some of the questions will have been addressed during the actual group discussion while other questions will require more introspection. Nevertheless, the purpose of having the participants write out their answers is to reinforce the lesson's key points and any personal discoveries.

The Number of Sessions: **Responsibly Driven** created this curriculum with a set number of sessions; however, that does not mean that actual delivery of facilitation cannot be augmented. Facilitators may have to double or triple the number of sessions per lesson to satisfy the legal variance of class lengths. Increasing the number of group sessions is beneficial since it grants more opportunity for personal discovery.

CS3 Sobriety Plan: The *CS3 Sobriety Plan* is a central component to the *Responsibly Driven: An Impaired Driving Prevention Curriculum*. When an opportunity arises, facilitators are to incorporate its four components - *clean, sober, safe,* and *sustainable* - into the group discussions. Also, facilitators should be prepared to share their own *CS3 Sobriety Plan* when discussing the *CS3 Sobriety Plan*. This gesture demonstrates the value of the CS3 Sobriety Plan and its practical application. Facilitators are in a critical position in which they can model the concepts and values of **Responsibly Driven.**

"Way of Being"

Responsibly Driven strongly encourages facilitators to be vigilant of their "way of being". A person's "ways of being" is their posture towards another human and/or situation. It is an attitude communicated verbally or nonverbally. Although these messages are often relayed without one's awareness, they convey more meaning than one's professed message.

We emphasize three components that will enhance a facilitator's ability to stay grounded in a "way of being" that maximizes the experience of the participants: humility, generosity, and authenticity.

Humility – Consider the following two points when contemplating humility:

An acknowledgement of one's own fallibility: By admitting one's capability to make mistakes and/or far short of his/her goals and expectations, facilitators can experience a closer affinity to the participants and their struggles.

A humble "way of being" exudes compassion and empathy: Facilitators who capture this posture create a context for the participants to experience their facilitator as someone who is "walking besides them" on their journey of personal discovery. It communicates a message of "being there for them."

Generosity – Mark Twain captured the essence of a generous leader when he offered the statement, "People don't care how much you know until they know how much you care." Participants experience a facilitator as generous when he/she is willing to give of his/herself. By being willing to share your life experiences, even the ones that put you in a bad light, a message of sincerity is projected. It is not about teaching or instruction. Your display of vulnerability provides the participants permission to be vulnerable. With such a presence, participants will more likely consider your perspectives, because they know you care about them and are invested in their futures.

Authenticity – Facilitators are most effective when they are honest, not only to others but also themselves. Such honesty requires deep introspection, the type that provides insight into one's momentary intentions. A common misstep of facilitators is losing focus of his/her purpose. When channeling authenticity a facilitator is able to stay grounded and focus on the participants' pressing needs rather than his/her momentary needs. The facilitator can also acknowledge the contributions (thoughts, emotions, and actions) that he/she is offering to the situational context (i.e., the group aura). Authenticity involves "keeping it real" with oneself by asking the questions, "What I am really up to? What is my purpose of saying this statement or behaving in this manner?" Modeling authenticity is the most important invitation that a facilitator can provide a participant. Authenticity transforms a person's "way of being" into an empowering presence, one that opens unlimited possibilities.

Listening

The most essential component to a conversation is listening; unfortunately, many people believe the contrary. Listening is exponentially more valuable to a facilitator than any other skill. Listening provides the vital resource that a facilitator needs to simulate a transformational conversation.

There are four types of listening skills that are critical to distinguish: appreciative listening, critical listening, relational listening, and discriminative listening (Bell n. pag.).

<u>Appreciative Listening</u> is a mode of enjoyment. It is when a person listens to another person's words or music's sound is an uncritical manner. The purpose of this listening skill is entertainment.

<u>Critical Listening</u> is a mode of analysis. It involves the identification of key points and/or arguments; in addition, the listener seeks to solidify his/her beliefs and judgments. Often critical listening is a selfish and suspicious style of listening because the person searches for avenues to prove his/herself "right".

<u>Relational Listening</u>, also known as therapeutic or empathetic listening, is one of the most valuable skills of listening. Ask yourself, "Is it more important to be understood or to understand?" **Responsibly Driven** asserts that the answer is "to understand". That is the purpose of relational listening, to be able to comprehend another person's words as if they were coming from your own mouth. Through that empathic connection the listener is able to identify the best means to support the other person. The listener is engaged in a conversation with an unselfish mindset, "I'm here for you."

<u>Discriminative Listening</u> is a skill that takes practice and intentionality. When employing Discriminative listening the listener seeks to hear the "unsaid" message(s). It is the ability to read between the lines without prejudice. Discriminative listening requires a disciplined ear and vigilant mind. The listener must maintain attention throughout the conversation: 1) by noticing the words and body language of the speaker; and 2) by remaining vigilant of his/her thoughts and their impact on the present conversation.

Facilitators must utilize all listening skills; however, **Responsibly Driven** encourages facilitators to strengthen their relationship and discriminative listening skills. It is these two listening skills that will strengthen group rapport and provide the most resource for participants' personal growth.

Feedback

Responsibly Driven relies heavily on feedback from both the facilitators and the participants. Feedback can be defined as, "an expression of a person's experience of a situation or another individual". Feedback is always available to us. It comes in many different forms: verbal communication, body language, facial expressions, eye contact, laughter, tears, inaction, etc. Feedback allows us to identify how we are "showing up" to a person or in a situation. Granted people ultimately are responsible for how they interpret a given situation; however, we can individually become more effective in our lives when we are open to understanding how we generate situational contexts. Feedback is the "breakfast of champions", because often people choose to be irresponsible and are unwilling to analyze the effects of their behavior on others. The nature of a champion demands a will to improve through the courageous sacrifice of cherished short-term gains.

Example: Johnny offers a comment that I am acting aggressive and selfish. If my intention is to be a "good friend" and Johnny offered that feedback, then I am apparently not being effective, in the moment, of generating a context of "being good friend". Johnny presented some valuable information. Am I willing to consider how Johnny's experience of selfishness and aggressiveness was created? It is easy to be irresponsible. To be responsible requires energy, honesty, humility, and courage. I could dismiss Johnny's feedback and blame his experience totally on him; basically, washing my hands of the situation. However, if I am committed to be "being a good friend" and do not want to generate an experience of selfishness and aggressiveness, then I must bravely ponder the question: "What am I doing or not doing that is being perceived as aggressive and selfish?" Johnny presented a wonderful opportunity. I can reaffirm my commitment of "being a good friend" by shifting my posture towards Johnny and choosing to behave in a way that conforms to my definition of a "good friend". This same sort of inquiry is available for all relational dynamics.

Responsibly Driven utilizes feedback as a tool for participants to discover their effectiveness in producing their professed intentions. Most people will declare that they never intended to be a part of an impaired driving class; yet, the result of their enrollment suggests otherwise. As facilitators, we invite participants to courageously explore their past behavior, thoughts, attitudes, and beliefs in hopes of identifying how they had been "showing up" that produced the result of mandated impaired driving classes. We further encourage them to clarify their intentions and behave in accordance with them. This process requires a level of vigilance and diligence. If our intentions are as important as we declare, then we should be willing to commit such behaviors that will bring them to fruition.

Things to Consider When Giving Feedback:

Solicit Approval – It is important to receive a person's permission to offer feedback prior to giving it. Unsolicited feedback is often rejected merely based on the objection that it was unwelcomed. A person is more likely to be receptive to your comments if you first gain their approval. By asking for approval, you can determine if the person wants feedback and is an open channel.

Know Your Purpose – Check in with yourself by pondering the reasons you want to offer feedback. Are you seeking to sow value into the participant, or are you simply looking for a way to prove yourself right, to assert control, to feel good, or to look good? These examples are only some disingenuous reasons why we offer feedback. It is a selfish posture. Feedback is about the participant, not you. Facilitators are encouraged to stay vigilant of their purpose, especially when offering feedback.

Come with a Posture of Compassion – As mentioned above, feedback is for the person receiving it. When a person is not grounded in this purpose, feedback can become weaponized. It can damage the receiving person and the relationship between the two people when not offered in a compassionate manner, a posture of care. **Responsibly Driven** believes that the relationship between the facilitator(s) and participants is priceless and must be nurtured. Facilitators are responsible for creating a group dynamic that is welcoming and open for personal growth. This sort of situational context can be created when the person offering feedback is grounded in a posture of compassion.

Fight for Maximum Value – Opportunities come and opportunities goes. Facilitators are strongly encouraged to introduce a sense of urgency into the group sessions. A participant may present an opening for a very important area for inquiry, so facilitators need to be receptive to such invitations. If the movement is missed, it is likely that the participant may shut down or that particular matter may never arise again, hence a pivotal junction is missed.

Things to Consider When Receiving Feedback:

Responsibly Driven suggests that facilitators should introduce the concept of feedback to participants as soon as it is appropriate in the group sessions. Offering feedback is only one side of the coin. Receiving feedback is just as important as giving it. It is just as true for the participants as it is for the facilitators. Receiving feedback requires courage, honesty, and humility.

Courage is required because one must be willing to hear another's experience of him/herself and to face things that may be unflattering .

Honesty is necessary because one must be open to considering the validity of the feedback and then be willing to look deep into oneself.

Humility is vital because one must acknowledge his/herself's humanity. We are all humans and have blind spots. When these blind spots come up there is temptation to be defensive and to protect our ego and pride. The reality is that there will be times we will simply miss things. We must be willing to ask for feedback at times in order to gain clarity on the things we don't know that we don't know. Case in point, ask yourself, "If I had food on my teeth and did not know it, would I like someone to point it out?"

Introduction: "How Did I Get Here?"	
Objective:	The primary purpose of this introductory session is to welcome participants, to create a situational context conducive for group rapport development, and to clearly outline the program, its expectations, and its goals.

Schedule:	**10 Minutes – Group Welcome**
	    Lesson Quote:
	    If you want something you've never had, then you've got to do something you've never done. Thomas Jefferson
	
	        Ask participants for their interpretation of the quote. Then connect it in with **Responsibly Driven's** mission.
	
	        This quote is similar to the contemporary definition of insanity, doing the same thing over again and expecting different results. **Responsibly Driven** invites participants into a "new way of relating" to their life experiences in order to identify the most effective perspective to achieve one's aspirations.
	
	15 Minutes – Program Introduction
	    <u>**Responsibly Driven's** Mission</u>
	    To promote responsibility and honesty, develop integrity and intentionality, encourage sobriety, and increase self-efficacy.
	
	    Program Structure
	    The program entails eleven hour and half sessions, including this introduction, in which participants will engage in group discussions and activities. Writing assignments will be given at the conclusion of each lesson. To earn a program completion, participants will be required to complete the assignments and the *CS3 Sobriety Plan*.
	
	    Group Rules and Expectations:
	    Confidentially must be strictly observed by all members. What is said in the group stays in the group.
	    Be respectful of one another.
	    Keep your sharing focused on yourself.
	    No side-talk. Side-talk is when two or more individuals engage in conversation with themselves separate from the group.
	    Be willing to try out new perspectives and tools.
	    Be open to feedback.
	
	15 Minutes – Introductions
	    Facilitators' Introductions
	    Share with the group your name, experience, and reason(s) for facilitating.
	
	    Participants' Introductions
	    Ask participants to share their names and a personal fun fact or positive attribute.
	
	5 Minutes – Presentation of Lesson's Concepts
	    Critical Points:
	    Impaired driving is a 100% preventable crime.

Impaired driving is a series of choices.
Self-effort is the only means of producing a lasting sobriety. The participants must do the necessary work to effect positive change in their life.
The foundation to **Responsibly Driven's** program is the *CS3 Sobriety Plan* and it rests on four components: *clean, sober, safe,* and *sustainable.*

5 Minutes – Presentation of *CS3 Sobriety Plan*'s Four Components
CLEAN: I will abstain from behaviors that could be harmful to my health.
SOBER: I will avoid actions that adversely impair my judgment. Above all, I will strive to maintain a clear mind.
SAFE: I will avoid actions that could put my life or the lives of others at risk.
SUSTAINABLE: I will work to maintain long-term sobriety that is a natural part of my life.

25 Minutes – Group Discussion
Essential Questions:
What are you looking to get out of this program?
What will it take for you to achieve those goals?
Describe your substance use.
Describe your experience(s) with impaired driving.
Finish the following sentence with a few words (one to two sentences):
   "The reason(s) I decided to finally get help. . ."
What is your idea of sobriety?

10 Minutes – Landing Point
If you do not like the results you are receiving in life, you have the opportunity and ability to choose a new perspective to assist you in becoming more effective in fulfilling your life commitments and aspirations.

10 Minutes – Check Out
Ask each member to briefly state how they related to the lesson.
Distribute the handbook and instruct the participants to complete the Introduction's questions before the next group.

Lesson 1: Honesty	
Objective:	Facilitators are to explain the importance of honesty and its role in recovery in addition to supporting participants' development of honesty's practical application in their lives. Facilitators are also to assist participants in discovering the value of seeing their actions from another person's perspective.

Schedule:	**15 Minutes – Group Check-In**
	    Check-In Question: What is one thing about you that we do not know?
	
	        Because it is early in the group, it is a good idea to ask a question that allows groups members to get to know each other. This approach will help participants feel more comfortable in the group, therefore increasing their willingness to be more candid about their issues with impaired driving.
	
	    Lesson Quote:
	    Honesty is an active verb, not a passive noun. Go out of your way to be truthful, beginning with the things that you say to yourself. Joe Tye
	
	        Ask participants for their interpretation of the quote. Then connect it to the lesson.
	
	        This quote emphasizes intentional steps each person must take if they want to become more honest with themselves and in their relationships.
	
	10 Minutes – Presentation of Lesson Concepts
	    Critical Points:
	    Honesty is the foundation of positive change.
	    Honesty gives you a connection with something greater than yourself. Lies separate us from reality and lead to greater harm.
	    We must create a mindset that supports honesty.
	
	15 Minutes – Group Discussion on Lesson
	    Essential Questions:
	    What is honesty to you?
	    Why should you practice honesty in your life?
	
	15 Minutes – Honesty Exercise
	    Ask participants to visualize the last time they drove intoxicated. During this visualization ask participants to see themselves through the eyes of another person. The person could be an older version of themselves, another person they know and trust, or perhaps a historical figure whose character stood out to them. As they watch themselves through the eyes of this other person, ask them to reflect on their actions and the mindset they created that allowed them to drive impaired.
	
	    Materials Needed: A timer/stopwatch, two pieces of paper, and pencil/pen for each participant
	
	15 Minutes – Group Discussion of the Honesty Exercise
	    Exercise Questions:
	    Describe the experience of seeing yourself drive impaired through another person's eyes.

Did the opinion of your action change when viewing it from a different perspective. Explain.

Whose viewpoint is more accurate, and why?

10 Minutes – Landing Point

There is no growth without honesty. When we are honest with ourselves, we can discern our shortcomings and treat them before they harm ourselves or others. Also, we will find positive attributes and emotions that can be used to build happier, healthier lives. It may be difficult to be honest but having the capacity to discern "What is true?", in any situation, demonstrates exactly the kind of strength and courage needed to enact real change in our lives.

10 Minutes – Check Out

Ask each member to briefly state how they related to the lesson.

Instruct the participants to complete <u>Session One's</u> questions before the next group.

Lesson 2: Denial	
Objective:	In this lesson, we define denial, its effect on our judgement, and how it affects the choices we make in the context of impaired driving. We also explain the powerful allure of denial and our resistance to recognize truth; in addition, we then provide useful tools to identify and dispel our denials.

Schedule:	**15 Minutes – Group Check-In**
	    Check-In Question: How has the last gathering about honesty impacted you?
	
	        Because it is early in the group, facilitators should use this question to encourage participants to apply lessons learned from the curriculum in their everyday lives. A change in thinking should be followed with a change in action.
	
	    Lesson Quote:
	    Before you can lie to another, you must first lie to yourself. Naval Ravikant
	
	        Ask participants for their interpretation of the quote. Then connect it to the lesson.
	
	        This quote emphasizes the personal responsibility we have in accepting our denials. While in denial we develop a belief and accept it not because it is true, but because it enables us to do what we want to do.
	
	20 Minutes – Presentation of Lesson Concepts
	    Critical Points:
	    Denial is a system of false beliefs that are not based on reality.
	    Being wrong is difficult to admit because it conflicts with our self-image.
	    Addiction is not a necessary component of impaired driving. A person can be drinking for the first time and make the choice to drive home intoxicated.
	    If you, no matter how rare, become intoxicated and then make the choice to put your life and the lives of others at risk by driving impaired, you have a problem.
	
	35 Minutes – Group Discussion of Denial Lesson
	    Essential Questions:
	    What areas of your life do you believe denial is most active?
	    Give an example of a denial used to enable you to drive intoxicated?
	    Why is it so hard for us to admit we are wrong?
	
	10 Minutes – Landing Point
	        Every person who makes the choice to drive impaired has a problem. A rational person would never choose to put their life or the lives of others in danger by driving impaired. The key to preventing impaired driving is addressing our underlying issues. This process can only begin when we admit we have a problem.
	
	10 Minutes – Check Out
	        Ask each member to briefly state how they related to the lesson.
	        Instruct the participants to complete <u>Session Two's</u> questions before the next group.

	Lesson 3: Relationship with Alcohol, Drugs, and Impaired Driving	
Objective:	We examine four key areas–family, friends, entitlements/justifications, and self-identity–in this lesson to aid participants in understanding the relationships they entertained with alcohol and/or drugs. We use the term relationship to convey the many complex connections we have with our substance use.	

Schedule:	**15 Minutes – Group Check-In**
	     Check-In Question: What is one reward you received from your substance use?
	
	     This question is used to provide some background information into each participants substance use. The use of the word reward is critical because it allows participants believe that they benefitted from their substance use.
	
	     Lesson Quote:
	     A belief is not merely an idea the mind possesses, it is an idea that possesses the mind. Robert Oxten Bolt
	
	     Ask participants for their interpretation of the quote. Then connect it to the lesson.
	
	     This quote can be used to underscore the importance of our beliefs and the reason(s) we must examine them to uncover false beliefs that have led us to harm ourselves and others.
	
	 20 Minutes – Presentation of Lesson Concepts
	     Critical Points:
	     We all have a relationship with our substance of choice. This relationship has a history filled with thoughts, feelings, and beliefs.
	     From an early age, we develop ideas about drug and alcohol use from our family.
	     Social life plays a huge part in our choice to drive impaired. For example, most people drive intoxicated after drinking with friends.
	     Entitlements/Justifications are excuses we use to make us feel we have the right to do something.
	     We each have a picture of ourselves when we drink alcohol/use drugs. Most often, the idea we have about ourselves while intoxicated and reality are two very different things.
	
	 35 Minutes – Group Discussion on Relationship with Alcohol, Drugs, and Impaired Driving Lesson
	     Essential Questions:
	     What did your family teach you about drinking alcohol/using drugs?
	     How do your friends influence your habits of drinking alcohol/using drugs? Explain.
	     What is an excuse you use to drink alcohol/use drugs?
	     What does drinking alcohol/using drugs "fix"?
	
	 10 Minutes – Landing Point
	     We cannot control what we do not understand, therefore, we must seek to comprehend the issues that underlie our destructive behavior, such as impaired driving.	

	10 Minutes – Check Out
	Ask each member to briefly state how they related to the lesson.
	Instruct the participants to complete <u>Session Three's</u> questions before the next group.

Lesson 4: Responsibility and Underlying Issues	
Objective:	A person who gets behind the steering wheel of a car and then drives intoxicated has made not just one, but several irresponsible choices. We have a responsibility to ourselves and to our communities to understand why we choose to drive impaired. We present four questions that will help participants uncover their underlying issues with impaired driving.
Schedule:	**15 Minutes – Group Check-In** Check-In Question: What does *responsibility* mean to you? This question is used to begin a conversation about *responsibility*. Facilitators should use participants' answers to reframe *responsibility* in the context of an individual's personal responsibility to uncover and address their issues with driving under the influence. Lesson Quote: *If we change within, our outer life will change also.* Jean Shinoda Bolen Ask participants for their interpretation of the quote. Then tie it to the lesson. Change begins inward and is achieved when it is put into action. Facilitators should use this quote to encourage participants towards real tangible change that can be seen in how participants think about themselves and in the choices they make. It is not enough to think differently, we must also act differently. **20 Minutes – Presentation of Lesson Concepts** Critical Points: A responsible person makes informed, prosocial choices based upon a rational understanding of the world. A responsible person takes ownership of the choices he/she makes and the outcomes of his/her choices. A responsible person does not put others or him/herself in dangerous situations by driving under the influence of mind-altering substances. Impaired driving is a series of choices. We make a choice to become intoxicated, and then another choice to drive impaired. Knowing why we drove impaired is about understanding the feelings, influences, and ultimately the beliefs that facilitated that choice. **35 Minutes – Group Exercise on the Four Questions** Arrange participants into groups of two. If there is an odd number of participants then the facilitator can pair up with a participant. Each participant will be given three minutes to answer each one of the following questions. Facilitators shall monitor the time and instruct participants as to what question they should be answer. Participants who are not speaking are instructed to listen and not to give feedback. Essential Questions: What do I believe? What do I feel? What is going on in the moment? What is stopping my change?

As a group, discuss participants' answers and their perspectives on the exercise and the lesson's concepts. Facilitators can use this as an opportunity to guide participants into deeper levels of understanding and their choice to drive impaired.

10 Minutes – Landing Point

Self-knowledge is the key to positive change. Until we come to an understanding of ourselves—why we make the choices we make, why we feel the way we do, and how we choose to deal with those emotions—we will not have the self-control needed to ensure we never drive impaired again.

10 Minutes – Check Out

Ask each member to briefly state how they related to the lesson.

Instruct the participants to complete <u>Session Four's</u> questions before the next group.

	Lesson 5: "Is It Safe for Me to Drink Again?"
Objective:	Impaired drivers operated with a distorted belief system that finds an array of excuses to justify driving intoxicated. In this session, we assist participants in the examination of their impaired driving history and their decision to continue drinking alcohol and/or using drugs.

Schedule:	**15 Minutes – Check-In**
	
	Check-In Question: What belief(s) are hindering you from achieving your life aspirations?
	
	The question helps us uncover the beliefs that perpetuates our self-destructive behaviors, especially impaired driving, and diminishes our ability to maximize our potential in life.
	
	Lesson Quote:
	"Chapters of My Life"
	
	Chapter 1: I walk down the street. There is a deep hole in the sidewalk. I fall in. I am lost . . . I am helpless . . . It wasn't my fault. It takes forever to find a way out.
	
	Chapter 2: I walked down the same street. There is a deep hole in the sidewalk. I pretend that I don't see it. I fall in again. I can't believe that I am in the same place again, but it's not my fault. It still takes a long time to get out.
	
	Chapter 3: I walked down the same street. There is a deep hole in the sidewalk. I see it is there. I still fall in . . . it is a habit. My eyes are open. I know where I am. . It is my fault. I get out immediately.
	
	Chapter 4: I walked down the same street. There is a deep hole in the sidewalk. I walk around it. I don't fall in the hole.
	
	Chapter 5: I chose to walk down another street. Portia Nelson
	
	Ask the participants for their interpretation of the quote. Then connect it to the lesson.
	
	This quote captures the tortuous process of cognitive and behavioral change Far too often, we often resist new perspectives and change even when reality reveals the errors and consequences of our thoughts and beliefs.
	
	5 Minutes – Presentation of Lesson's Concepts
	Critical Points:
	Many people can and do drink responsibly; however, we, at **Responsibly Driven,** believe it is <u>not safe</u> for you to drink, if you. . .
	    Have substance dependency issues,
	    Have a history of impaired driving (regardless of whether you were caught),
	    Have hurt another person (including yourself) intoxicated,
	    Have not addressed your underlying issues.

Responsibly Driven believes the concept of "using responsibly" applies only in states that have legalized recreational or medicinal drug use.

Abstinence is the voluntary cessation from the use of drugs or alcohol.

Be open to the opportunities and positive changes abstinence can bring to your life.

45 Minutes – Group Discussion on "Is It Safe for Me to Drink Again?" Lesson
<u>Essential Questions:</u>
What are the reasons do you profess to continue to drive impaired?
Why are the legal consequences insufficient to deter you from driving impaired?
Will you choose to abstain from alcohol or to drink alcohol responsibly? (Explain your choice.)
> If you answered, "to drink responsibly," why have you not drank alcohol responsibly in the past? What has changed?
> If you answered, "to abstain," what will your life look like sober?
> What internal and external work is needed for abstinence to become a natural part of our life?

10 Minutes – Landing Point
It is not safe to drink alcohol or use legal drugs for individuals who have substance dependency issues, a history of impaired driving, hurt another person (including his/herself) intoxicated, and/or not addressed his/her underlying issues.

10 Minutes – Check Out
Ask each member to briefly state how they related to the lesson.
Instruct the participants to complete <u>Session Five's</u> questions before the next group.

Lesson 6: Personal Sobriety	
Objective:	We explore ways to gain personal sobriety through an understanding of self, which allows us to address our needs in a healthy and constructive way. With this understanding, we ask that participants begin to create an individualized sobriety plan that is *clean, sober, safe,* and *sustainable*.

Schedule:	**15 Minutes –Check-In**
	 Check-In Question: What does sobriety look like to you?
	
	 Participants are asked how their version of sobriey looks like in action. Importantly, this may include responsible drinking. It is important that participants are given permission to answer in whatever way they feel is true for them.
	
	 Lesson Quote:
	 You cannot solve a problem from the same consciousness that created it. You must learn to see the world anew. Albert Einstein
	
	 Ask participants for their interpretation of the quote. Then tie it to the lesson.
	
	 The addictive personality romanticizes intoxication while failing to fully appreciate its negative consequences, hence we typically repeat our destructive behaviors such as impaired driving. **Responsibly Driven,** through its *CS3 Sobriety* Plan, offers a roadmap for the life we desire.
	
	20 Minutes – Presentation of Personal Sobriety Lesson
	 Critical Points:
	 Abstinence does not address the underlying issues of why a person abused substance(s) or made irresponsible choices in the first place.
	 We will continue to have problems until we address the underlying issues that fueled our substance abuse.
	 A sobriety plan is a success plan. It gives us a means to understand and deal with urges as they arise, while also building a foundation for personal growth, improved health, and wellness.
	 Responsibly Driven asks participants to create a sobriety plan that demonstrates the following components:
	
	  CLEAN: I will abstain from behaviors that could be harmful to my health.
	  SOBER: I will avoid actions that adversely impair my judgment. Above all, I will strive to maintain a clear mind.
	  SAFE: I will avoid actions that could put my life or the lives of others at risk.
	  SUSTAINABLE: I will work to maintain long-term sobriety that is a natural part of my life.
	
	30 Minutes – Group Discussion
	 Essential Questions:
	 What did your substance abuse "fix"?
	 What will you do now to fulfill that need?
	 What did impaired driving "fix"?
	 What will you do now to fulfill that need?

As a group, review the concepts of *clean, sober, safe, and sustainable*, as defined by **Responsibly Driven,** and how they relate to participants' sobriety plans. Discuss whether these changes are reasonable and achievable.

10 Minutes – Landing Point
We are not looking for the "right" answer. We are looking for your "right" answer; an answer that addresses your individual issues and is *clean, sober, safe,* and *sustainable*.

10 Minutes – Check Out:
Ask each member to briefly state how they related to the lesson.
Instruct the participants to complete <u>Session Six's</u> questions before the next group.
Remind participants to work on their *CS3 Sobriety Plans*.

Lesson 7: From the Impaired Driving Survivor's Perspective	
Objective:	This is the first of a two-part series in which facilitators are expanding participants' capacity to exercise empathy for impaired driving victims and survivors. We explore impaired driving's impact on four life areas and the difficult journey survivors must endure to heal.
Schedule:	**15 Minutes – Check-In** 　　Check-In Question: What is better "to understand" or "to be understood"? 　　　　This question leaves many individuals conflicted. The answer we offer is "to understand", because far too often we entertain conversations with the purpose of conveying our points, which prevents us from understanding the other person's experience. 　　Lesson Quote: 　　*We think we listen, but very rarely do we listen with real understanding, true empathy. Yet listening, of this very special kind, is one of the most potent forces for change that I know.* Carl Rogers 　　　　Ask participants for their interpretation of the quote. Then tie it to the lesson. 　　　　People are willing to heed one's words when they feel that the other person truly cares about their well-being. Active listening is one of the purest examples of compassion and empathy because it validates another person's experience. **15 Minutes – Presentation of Lesson's Concepts** 　　Critical Points: 　　Impaired driving survivors and victims are impacted in four areas: Physical, Emotional, Financial, and Spiritual. 　　There are five elements that assist in the healing process of survivors: Safety, Empowerment, Restitution, Apology, and Answers. **45 Minutes – Group Discussion** 　　Essential Questions: 　　Who is affected by your decision to drive impaired? 　　How has identifying the wide reach of impaired driving's consequences affected your decision-making? 　　Which area of impact has the greatest effect on impaired driving survivors and victims? Why? 　　Can an impaired driving survivor live a fulfilling life without obtaining the "Five Elements of the Recovery Process?" Why or why not? **10 Minutes – Landing Point** 　　Crime, especially impaired driving, affects people in an array of ways. When we hurt somebody while driving intoxicated, we fundamentally alter that person's world and, in some ways, irreparably. We seek to help participants to develop empathy because it is a powerful transformative that stimulates positive personal growth. **10 Minutes – Check Out** 　　Ask each member to briefly state how they related to the lesson.

| | | Instruct the participants to complete <u>Session Seven's</u> questions before the next group. |
| | | Remind participants to continue working on their *CS3 Sobriety Plans*. |

Lesson 8: From the Impaired Driving Survivor's Perspective	
Objective:	This is the second of the two-part series in which facilitators are expanding the participants' capacity to exercise empathy for impaired driving victims and survivors. We dive deeper into the survivor's experience, first through a guided meditation and then through a recitation of several actual survivors' testimonials.

Schedule:	**15 Minutes – Check-In**
	
	Check-In Question: What does empathy mean to you?
	
	The purpose of this question is to generate background information on the participants' understanding of empathy and their personal experiencing of it.
	
	Lesson Quote:
	Empathy is allowing someone else's pain into your heart. Jim Micheletti
	
	Ask participants for their interpretation of the quote. Then tie it to the lesson.
	
	When attempting to truly understanding another person's suffering, it is more effective to fully immerse oneself into his /her worldview by adopting all his/her personal experiences and beliefs.
	
	5 Minutes – Presentation of Lesson's Concepts
	Critical Points:
	One choice to drive intoxicated can irreparably alter many people's lives.
	Lives are at stake every time you choose to drive impaired.
	The choice to drive impaired cannot be taken back.
	
	5 Minutes – Guided Meditation Exercise
	Before beginning the meditation ask the participants to ground themselves by placing their feet on the ground and taking several deep breaths. Once you are assured that everyone is relaxed read the visualization story. Take your time reading the passage and pausing appropriately. We want to make sure the participants identify with the driver's character in the story. Allow the participants to ponder their thoughts for several minutes after you concluded the recitation.
	
	Materials Needed: A timer/stopwatch, two pieces of paper, and pencil/pen for each participant.
	
	15 Minutes – Group Discussion on the Guided Meditation Exercise
	Essential Questions:
	Describe your experience based on the guided meditation exercise.
	    As the impaired driving survivor, what thoughts and feelings surfaced during this exercise?
	    As the impaired driver,
	        Why did you choose to drive impaired?
	        What would your reaction be to the news that you injured and/or killed a person while driving impaired?

5 Minutes – Recitation of Survivors' Testimonials
Before beginning the recitation, again ask the participants to ground themselves by placing their feet on the ground and taking several deep breathes. Once you are assured that everyone is relaxed read the first survivor excerpt. Take your time reading each excerpt while pausing for emphasis. Allow the participants to ponder their thoughts for a minute after each excerpt.

15 Minutes – Group Discussion on the Survivors' Testimonials
Essential Questions:
Describe your experience hearing the testimonials of the survivors and other individuals impacted by impaired driving.
- What are your thoughts, emotions, and reactions compare to that of the survivor?
- How were they different?
- What insights did you gain from the survivors' testimonials?
- How has this experience affected your view about your past choices to drive impaired?
- How will this experience influence your future choice to drive impaired?

10 Minutes – Landing Point
The development of empathy is expedited when one effectively internalized the experience of another person. When accurately adopting another person's perspective, we can begin to comprehend the real impact that our decisions have on his/her life.

10 Minutes – Check Out
Ask each member to briefly state how they related to the lesson.
Instruct the participants to complete Session Eight's questions before the next group.
Remind participants to complete their *CS3 Sobriety Plans* and to prepare for its presentation at the next group session.

Lesson 9: *CS3 Sobriety Plan* **Preparation**	
Objective:	The *CS3 Sobriety Plan* is the cornerstone of **Responsibly Driven's** program. Over the last couple of weeks participants have been working on their plans. In this lesson, facilitators are sharpening the participants' rough drafts by answering questions and clarifying the plan's purpose and concepts.

Schedule:	**15 Minutes – Check-In**
	    Check-In Question: Why is it important to create a plan?
	
	    This question is meant to reveal the importance of creating an action plan to prevent future impaired driving.
	
	15 Minutes – Opening Quotation
	    The future depends on what we do with the present. Mohandas K. Gandhi
	
	    Ask participants for their interpretation of the quote. Then tie it to the lesson.
	
	    We control our choices in the present moment, so it is imperative we act with intentionality to ensure we are moving towards our desired future.
	
	5 Minutes – Presentation of CS3 Sobriety Plan Preparation Lesson
	    Critical Points:
	    When you seek success you must construct a plan.
	    What you get out life is determined by what you invest into it.
	    CS3 Sobriety Plan is an important tool to construct a solid foundation for positive transformation.
	    No one's *CS3 Sobriety Plan* is the same. Each plan is specific to his/her life's circumstances.
	    The bottom line is we must find a solution to each of our problems, i.e., your underlying issues.
	    Directly address your underlying issues with a personalized plan that is tailored to your specific needs.
	
	45 Minutes – Group Discussion
	    Review *CS3 Sobriety Plan*'s four components:
	        CLEAN: I will abstain from behaviors that could be harmful to my health.
	        SOBER: I will avoid actions that adversely impair my judgment. Above all, I will strive to maintain a clear mind.
	        SAFE: I will avoid actions that could put my life or the lives of others at risk.
	        SUSTAINABLE: I will work to maintain long-term sobriety that is a natural part of my life.
	
	    Facilitators are encouraged to offer their *CS3 Sobriety Plans* as a practical example. Solicit and answer clarifying questions about the *CS3 Sobriety Plan* Briefly preview the presentation process.
	
	10 Minutes – Landing Point
	    The *CS3 Sobriety Plan* is an opportunity for the participants to account for their past decisions and prepare for their future. Without a plan, we are more

	likely to resort to old behavior patterns, hence continuing our lives of mediocrity. **10 Minutes – Check Out** Ask each member to briefly state how they related to the lesson. Remind participants to finish their *CS3 Sobriety Plans* for next week's group presentations.

Lesson 10: *CS3 Sobriety Plan* **Presentations**	
Objective:	The *CS3 Sobriety Plan* grants participants an opportunity to account for their past self-destructive behavior (e.g., impaired driving) and its negative impact on their friends, family, and community. It is also an important step in the process of personal development. Facilitators are to create a group context that encourages presenters to be authentic in their account and open to group feedback while assisting group members in becoming courageous and supportive in their feedback delivery.

Schedule:	**15 Minutes – Check-In**
	   <u>Check-In Question:</u> How was the process of preparing for your *CS3 Sobriety Plan* presentations?
	
	   Use this question to "break the ice". Participants are likely to be quite anxious about presenting their plans in front of the group, so utilize this opportunity to ease their tension.
	
	15 Minutes – Opening Quotation
	   In the time of your life, live. William Saroyan
	
	      Ask participants for their interpretation of the quote. Then tie it to the lesson.
	
	      This quote speaks to the truth that the past is the past and today is the first day of our new life. Let's act with vigor and urgency to maximize our human experience.
	
	5 Minutes – Presentation of *CS3 Sobriety Plan* Lesson
	   <u>Critical Points:</u>
	   Sobriety is a lifestyle. It is an attitude and a way of life that touches every part of our lives.
	   Your sobriety must be *clean, sober, safe,* and *sustainable.*
	   You must constantly adjust your *CS3 Sobriety Plan.*
	   Having a support network and being willing to ask for help are key strategies for staying sober.
	
	45 Minutes – *CS3 Sobriety Plans* Presentations
	   Briefly review *CS3 Sobriety Plan*'s four components:
	      CLEAN: I will abstain from behaviors that could be harmful to my health.
	      SOBER: I will avoid actions that adversely impair my judgment. Above all, I will strive to maintain a clear mind.
	      SAFE: I will avoid actions that could put my life or the lives of others at risk.
	      SUSTAINABLE: I will work to maintain long-term sobriety that is a natural part of my life.
	   Present the *CS3 Sobriety Plan* Presentation Instructions.
	      Refer to "Lesson 10: *CS3 Sobriety Plan* Presentations."
	
	10 Minutes – Check Out
	   Ask the participants to identify one experience that stood out to them in this program.

| | | Congratulate the participants for completing **Responsibly Driven's** *CS3 Sobriety Plan* and their participation throughout the weeks. Encourage the participants to continue working on and living their sobriety plans. |

APPENDIX C: PERSONAL TESTIMONIALS

PERSONAL TESTIMONIAL 1

Eric D.

In October 2005, while driving intoxicated, I struck and killed a police officer as he was conducting a freeway closure shortly after four o'clock in the morning. He was twenty-nine years old.

I made the choice to drive intoxicated despite knowing the dangers of driving under the influence (DUI) and being warned by others that I was too intoxicated to drive. I didn't have to make this choice. I could have gone out with friends and decided not to drink. I could have drunk responsibly. I could have taken a cab home. I could have slept at a friend's house. There were thousands of choices I could have made that night instead of driving home intoxicated. Yet, I choose to disregard the danger of my actions, the warnings of others, and plain common sense and chose to drive while intoxicated.

At that time, leaving my car overnight at a bar was too inconvenient. I had places that I needed to go, and I didn't want to pay for a taxi; I didn't want to be bothered with making plans to get home safe. Why should I? *I drove drunk hundreds of times before and nothing had happened.* This time, I knew, would be just like all the other times…except it wasn't. It's difficult now, still coming to terms with the pain and loss I caused, to describe the appallingly selfish and destructive beliefs I created to justify my actions. I was willing to believe anything if it allowed me to do what I wanted.

In the end, what I feared more than DUI was change, and I lacked the courage to admit I had a problem. My hope is that this testimony will persuade others making similar choices to take the necessary steps to address their underlying issues with alcohol and the choices they make while under the influence.

When I was seventeen, I took my first drink of alcohol. It was from a bottle of wine that I shared with a friend on a beach. Afterwards, we stumbled to his car and my friend drove home while I played with the radio. When we reached my house, I crept up my driveway like a cat burglar, tiptoeing up the walkway as my friend looked on laughing. When I reached my front door, I peeked through a side window and turned back to give my friend an enthusiastic thumb up. He nodded his head and drove off as I slid inside, sneaking past my parent's bedroom door into my room where I collapsed onto the bed. That night I thought about how different I felt when I was intoxicated.

---

[8] Testimonials were previously published in *IMPACT: Insights, Effects and the Reality of Impaired Driving* by Fiesta Publishing, who generously gave permission for reprint.

Before I was always shy and hypersensitive around people. I obsessively worried about what others thought of me and tailored my behaviors accordingly. However, when I drank that night, I felt comfortable with where I was, who I was, and the people I was with. Where before I had always tried to avoid being noticed, now I wanted to be the center of attention. It was the quick fix I had been looking for. Instead of learning to work through my issues in an open and constructive way, I had found a way to temporarily *cure* myself.

As these thoughts raced through my head, I never stopped to contemplate the risk I created. My friend and I had not only drunk underage, but we had also driven home intoxicated. It was an hour and a half drive from the beach to my house. Our choice to drive intoxicated put everyone we encountered along the way at risk. I should have recognized the danger we created. Unfortunately, that night I felt no regret or fear for my actions; that would come later. Instead, what I remembered was a fun night with a friend, along with a newly formed belief that alcohol could make me feel the way I wanted to feel. Worst of all, I couldn't wait to feel that way again.

My drinking progressed after I entered the military. Now drinking wasn't just about helping me relax around people, it was a means of validating myself. I was tough if I could drink a lot of alcohol. It was cool to be seen with my friends at a bar with a drink in my hand. As shallow and self-centered as those pursuits were, they mattered to me, and I sought them out. I had many justifications for my actions. I always focused on certain areas of my life to convince myself that I was a good person. I told myself, I didn't have an alcohol problem because I never got a DUI, and because I was only a "social drinker." Over time, my beliefs grew more dysfunctional as I continued drinking and making dangerous choices. I believed that drinking and driving was wrong when other people did it, but not me. "I was a good driver; I was different; I didn't have a drinking problem." Nothing like the thousands of deaths caused by impaired driving every year could happen to someone like me; "I'm a good person."

It is shameful for someone to believe that his/her actions will not harm others because that person thinks him/herself to be important or special. That was me. I could have learned a lot from the officer I killed. He had only been an officer four short-years, yet he accomplished so much. On one occasion he saved a man who was pinned under a car. He lifted the car from the man's chest allowing him to breathe and held it there until help arrived. He received the Life Saving Effort Award and the Medal of Valor for his efforts. In 2004, he was awarded the Mothers Against Drunk Driver's (MADD) Hero Award for making the most driving under the influence (DUI) arrests in the county. He was the department's most productive officer and a member of the Special Weapons and Tactical Team (SWAT).

I was nothing like him. When I came back from deployments in the military, I brought back a sense of entitlement. I only thought of the things I felt others owed me, never about the responsibility I had to them or my community. My life stood in stark contrast to the officer's. I used my service in the military to justify my inexcusable behavior. I invested myself into drinking and partying. I was shallow and selfish. I put off my responsibilities in life, so I could have my time. I never thought about anyone else. Had I exercised the least bit of care or willingness to reflect on my character and actions, this officer's life would not have been cut short.

During my sentencing, many people testified about his character. They spoke how he positively affected their lives and the entire community. Every day he wore his uniform he put his life on the line with a sense of responsibility and gratitude toward his job and the people he served. He was the good person I pretended to be.

If you are reading this testimony and have made the choice to drive while intoxicated, then it is critical that you take an honest look at your substance use and the choices you are making. Whether it be in **Responsibly Driven**, Alcoholics Anonymous (AA), substance abuse treatment, or through trusted friends and family, please get the help you need to ensure that you never find yourself behind the wheel intoxicated. Deaths caused by driving under the influence are preventable. Your life and the lives of those who live in your community depend on it.

PERSONAL TESTIMONIAL 2

Jonathan B.

In 2003, I killed an innocent woman while driving under the influence (DUI) of alcohol and marijuana. I fled the scene of the collision without rendering aid to either her or her husband. Hours later the police apprehended me several miles down the highway. During my arrest, I told the officers, "It was only an accident…have some sympathy for me."

The way I ended that statement, *for me*, captures the essence of my attitude at that point in my life. Everything was about me; I believed that I was the center of the universe. This selfish perspective affected more than just my decision to drive while intoxicated. It was not until I broke down the different components of impaired driving that I was able to identify the extent of my poor decision-making.

Impaired driving is comprised of two different components: 1) the decision to use/drink mind-altering substances and 2) the decision to drive. First, I decided to use psychoactive substances during my adolescence. Instead of facing social anxiety in a responsible way, I embraced the numbing intoxication of alcohol and marijuana. These substances became my source of artificial courage. I denied the fact that I was dependent on these substances with layers of distorted beliefs. One such belief was my concept of *coolness*. As a teen, I believed it was cool to engage in adult activities such as drinking alcohol. I also believed it was cool to do things that were considered taboo, like smoking marijuana.

As time went on, I chose to associate with people who fit into my perspective of *coolness* and I desperately sought their acceptance. I also held the belief that using drugs and drinking alcohol were effective coping mechanisms. I believed that alcohol and drugs relieved my social anxiety;

hence, my self-image improved. In my mind, I would change from a nervous and insecure adolescent into an outgoing, handsome, and exciting man. With tempered nerves, I presumed that my goals of peer acceptance and admiration were achievable. When I was unsuccessful or felt socially rejected, I found solace in the immature thought, "So what, I'm drunk/high."

At the same time, driving recklessly factored into my view of what social acceptance looked like. As a pre-teen, I envisioned a future of freedom—a freedom to go and do whatever I wanted, a freedom that was dependent on obtaining my driver's license. I believed that a driver's license equated to manhood and a thriving social life. It wasn't *cool* to be driven around by one's parents. In addition, I believed *cool* meant being the person who drove everyone around. I believed that it was *cool* to claim to be the fastest driver. I believed driving around town, with my seat lowered and having only one hand on the steering wheel while listening to loud music, was *cool*. Those misguided beliefs lead me to believe it was paramount that I obtain both a license and a car. By adopting this frame of mind, I essentially reduced my personal value to a person who owns a car.

It was my fear of missing out on something that prompted my habit of driving dangerously. I convinced myself that to stay relevant; I had to be at every social function. If there were multiple parties in one night, I would rush from one side of Los Angeles County to the other. To a certain extent, it was a race between loneliness and me. A race in which I refused to slow down or pay attention to the stop signs. I frequently drove recklessly and exceedingly fast while taking numerous shortcuts and disregarding many traffic laws. I needed to make an appearance everywhere to ensure that people did not forget about or leave me behind.

Anytime the opportunity presented itself, I would get high on marijuana. Since I believed using drugs and alcohol enhanced my social life, it was inevitable that I would decide to drive intoxicated to *the next big thing*, wherever *it* was located. I told myself ridiculous stories that neither marijuana or alcohol impaired my motor skills. Therefore, after becoming intoxicated, I often made the poor decision to drive. Most of the time, I would even *hot-box* (driving around while my car filled up with marijuana smoke) on the way to a social gathering. I ignorantly believed it was *cool* to show up some place and have marijuana smoke creep out of my car as I exited. I convinced myself that what was wrong for others did not apply to me, especially driving impaired. I believed that I was above the law. I used this egotistical way of thinking to justify my decision to drive while intoxicated and impaired, thus meeting both the first and second components of a DUI.

When I began attending college, I expanded my substance abuse to include more serious drugs. Although I lived on campus and did not drive often, my mindset to engage in dangerous activities while intoxicated remained. The story I told myself was that the *college experience* necessitated that I adopt a hardcore party lifestyle of womanizing and *getting wasted*. Just like high school, my desire to be accepted surfaced. This reinforced what I believed had worked in the past—drinking alcohol and smoking marijuana. I took the party lifestyle even further in college because I believed that the harder I partied, the more social admiration I would gain.

My decision-making worsened after attending my first college. At that point in my life, I placed a lot of importance on having a car, so I could drive from place to place. My social network ranged from Southern to Central California, so my social relations rested on my ability to travel—at least that is what I told myself. With more parties to attend, I began to drive under the influence of an array of illicit substances. By that time, the decision to behave in such a dangerous and careless manner became effortless due to the mindset I had created.

Since I had been driving under the influence of marijuana and alcohol for years, the transition to drive under the influence of other drugs was seamless. Not only did I completely disregard the consequences of my choices, but I also became callous toward the welfare of others. My false sense of invincibility convinced me that the concept of safety did not apply to me. The story I told myself was, "I am an excellent driver, even when I am intoxicated. I would never be a character in one of those tragic DUI stories. I am special." As long as I was able to make the key turn the ignition switch, I was convinced that I could operate a motor vehicle.

I used delusions, justifications, and rationalizations to shape my perspective. The stories I concocted allowed me to remain in complete denial about my irresponsible actions. I simply dispersed the blame when the consequences of my decisions began to manifest because it was easier to divert responsibility. I would erroneously characterize my troubles as freak occurrences. When I was arrested for a drug bust, it was the police informant and my roommate's fault. When I was kicked out of college, it was the Resident Assistant's fault for improperly calling the police. When I clipped a car, it was because I was distracted when something fell off my dashboard. When I drove my car into the center-median, it was because I was overworked and tired. When I was arrested for a DUI, it was simply the result of having an empty stomach. Nothing was ever my fault. Accountability was virtually missing from my life.

Having a blackout was one of my favorite ways to avoid responsibility. I convinced myself that a memory lapse excused any personal accountability, as if the preceding night's events never occurred. When people recounted the previous night's events, I would typically laugh it off and offer a flippant response like, "I was drunk and high." The reality is I am ultimately responsible for everything that occurred during my blackouts because I consciously chose to drink and use. A blackout is not an excuse for anyone's actions.

It took years before I recognized how serious impaired driving was and even longer before I accepted responsibility for my past actions, specifically the murder of the married woman. I hid behind my delusions for several years, especially the one in which I told myself that her death was only an accident. The dangers of impaired driving are common knowledge. Before I took her life, I saw countless television commercials, drove past numerous billboards warning against this reckless behavior, and was given multiple admonitions by criminal justice officials. Therefore, I cannot claim that I was unaware of the inherent dangers of impaired driving. Although I pleaded ignorance in the past. I am now keenly aware that my DUI collision was not an accident.

In the presence of numerous indicators, I denied the fact that I was a dangerous person. These warning signs were constantly revealing the truth behind my intentions. My incessant decision to use drugs and alcohol was a warning sign. My series of traffic tickets were warning signs. My expulsion from college was a warning sign. My multiple police encounters were warning signs. My frequent blackout episodes were warning signs and, of course, my DUI arrest in May 2003 was the definitive warning sign. Nevertheless, I continued to ignore all those warning signs because I was unwilling to acknowledge that I was too self-centered, shallow, and selfish to own up to the consequences of my decisions. I did not believe that the laws of society applied to me. I was unwilling to face my former reality of immaturity, social anxiety, and addiction. I valued drugs, alcohol, and pleasure-based experiences over my family, my community, and my own well-being. I felt it was easier and more convenient to use a *quick fix* such as alcohol and marijuana than it was to deal with life's responsibilities.

No matter what we profess, our actions reveal our beliefs. This is why results are the true testament of one's intentions. DUIs do not simply just happen. For most of my life, I claimed that it was not my intention to drive impaired. However, based on my results and an honest reflection of my past belief system, I deliberately drove my car while impaired. The sad truth is it was only a matter of time before I killed someone. Upon this discovery, the connections between my past decisions and intentions became clear.

In 2003, I took a woman's life. I deprived her from having a future. I robbed her family of a loving wife and mother. I took a professor away from her college community. These reprehensible facts haunt me daily. She deserved much better, as did the thousands of other tragic DUI victims. Far too many people are killed each year in DUI collisions, and for what? Driving impaired is completely preventable. I chose to drive while intoxicated because I was a self-absorbed individual who thrived off artificial comfort and personal convenience at the expense of others. In the past, I was unwilling to acknowledge that I was the person who killed an innocent woman, the person who callously ran away from a loving husband who was holding his dying wife in his arms.

Today, I recognize I was that person, and I strive to make amends for the damage I have caused every day. I am committed to living a responsible life—one that is centered on others. A life that does not entertain the mentalities of selfishness and irresponsibility or the distorted thinking that impaired driving is okay.

APPENDIX D: TABLES

TABLE 1

BLOOD ALCOHOL CONCENTRATION (BAC) LEVELS[9]

[Table for Male (M) / Female (F)]

Number of Drinks		Body Weight in Pounds (lbs.)								Driving Conditions
		100	120	140	160	180	200	220	240	
0	M	0.00	0.00	0.00	0.00	0.00	0.00	0.00	0.00	Only Safe Driving Limit
	F	0.00	0.00	0.00	0.00	0.00	0.00	0.00	0.00	
1	M	0.06	0.05	0.04	0.04	0.03	0.03	0.03	0.02	Driving Skills Impaired
	F	0.07	0.06	0.05	0.04	0.04	0.03	0.03	0.03	
2	M	0.12	0.10	0.09	0.07	0.07	0.06	0.05	0.05	
	F	0.13	0.11	0.09	0.08	0.07	0.06	0.06	0.06	
3	M	0.18	0.15	0.13	0.11	0.10	0.09	0.08	0.07	Legally Intoxicated
	F	0.20	0.17	0.14	0.12	0.11	0.10	0.09	0.08	
4	M	0.24	0.20	0.17	0.15	0.13	0.12	0.11	0.10	
	F	0.26	0.22	0.19	0.17	0.15	0.13	0.12	0.11	
5	M	0.30	0.25	0.21	0.19	0.17	0.15	0.14	0.12	
	F	0.33	0.28	0.24	0.21	0.18	0.17	0.15	0.14	

Subtract 0.10% for each 40 minutes that lapse between drinks.

1 drink = 1.5 oz. 80 proof liquor, 12 oz. 5% beer, or 5 oz. 12 % wine

Fewer than 5 people out of 100 will exceed these values.

---

[9] State of California. Department of Motor Vehicles. *California Driver Handbook*. CA.Gov. N.d. Web. Dec. 2019. <https://www.dmv.ca.gov/portal/dmv/detail/pubs/hdbk/actions_aps_court>.

TABLE 2

THE PROGRESSIVE EFFECTS OF ALCOHOL CONSUMPTION[10]

BAC	BEHAVIOR	IMPAIRED FUNCTIONS
0.01-0.029	➢ Average individual appears normal	➢ Some subtle effects can be detected with special tests
0.03-0.59	➢ Mild euphoria ➢ Relaxation ➢ Joyousness ➢ Talkativeness ➢ Decreased inhibition	➢ Ability to concentrate diminished
0.06-0.99	➢ Blunted feelings ➢ Lack of inhibition ➢ Extraversion	➢ Reasoning impaired ➢ Depth perception skewed ➢ Peripheral vision diminished ➢ Glare recovery impaired
0.10-0.19	➢ Over-expression ➢ Emotional swings ➢ Anger or sadness ➢ Boisterousness ➢ Decreased sexual function	➢ Reflexes slowed ➢ Reaction time slowed ➢ Gross motor control diminished ➢ Likely to stagger ➢ Likely to slur speech
0.20-0.29	➢ Stupor Loss of understanding Impaired sensation	➢ Reduced respiration or periods where breathing stops ➢ Heart arrhythmia, irregular heartbeat
0.30-0.39	➢ Severe central nervous system depression ➢ Unconsciousness ➢ Death is possible	➢ Reduced ability to control bladder Breathing difficulties ➢ Heart rate abnormalities
0.40-0.50	➢ General inactivity or unresponsiveness ➢ Unconsciousness ➢ Death is possible	➢ Reduced respiration or periods where breathing stops ➢ Heart arrhythmia, irregular heartbeat
>.0.50	➢ Most individuals are dead by this point.	➢ Death

---

[10] Center for Wellness Promotion. "Progressive Effects of Alcohol Consumption". UNC Charlotte. N.d. Web. 30 Dec. 2019.
<https://wellness.uncc.edu/sites/wellness.uncc.edu/files/media/Stay%20In%20The%20Green%20BAC.pdf>.